BECOMING A
DISCIPLE-
MAKER

BECOMING A
DISCIPLE-MAKER

DEVELOP SPIRITUAL GROWTH SKILLS
AND HELP OTHERS TO DO THE SAME

BILLIE HANKS, JR.
with
RANDY CRAIG

INTERNATIONAL EVANGELISM ASSOCIATION
SALADO, TEXAS 76571

Becoming A Disciple-Maker Student's Guide
Copyright © 2013 by International Evangelism Association

For more information about this ministry, write or call:

INTERNATIONAL EVANGELISM ASSOCIATION
PO BOX 1174
SALADO, TEXAS 76571-1174
(254) 947-3030
www.ieaom.org

Printed in India

CONTENTS

Acknowledgements

For my wife Carol Anne's encouragement and the faithful prayers and support of International Evangelism's active and alumni board, I am deeply grateful. *Becoming A Disciple-Maker* represents a milestone in our growing understanding of how teaching and training work together in a healthy New Testament environment.

My personal thanks go to each staff member and intern who have made contributions toward this effort. In addition, I would like to especially thank Mr. Randy Craig for his tireless work, editing skills, and unwavering personal commitment to the vision of disciple-making. I am grateful for the creative and artistic gifts of Mr. Walt Wooden and Mr. Randy Ray for their support in typesetting and design. They have truly made this a labor dedicated to Christ.

The Godly examples and personal investment made in my life by Grady Wilson, Max Barnett, Gene Warr, Bev Shea, Wayne Watts, Roy Fish, T.W. Wilson, and Robert Coleman, are primarily where these insights were learned over the years. I thank God more than I can say for those men who have discipled me, plus Charlie Riggs, Howard Butt, and Billy Graham, for pointing the way on so many occasions.

My prayer is that each person who takes this course will be empowered by God to invest deeply in the lives of growing fellow believers and experience the great satisfaction that comes from serving the Lord Jesus Christ.

Yours in that joy,

Billie Hanks, Jr.

STUDENT'S GUIDE
INTRODUCTION

"...go make disciples of all nations..."
(Matthew 28:19)

Welcome to one of Christianity's most rewarding teaching experiences. This course's unique relational format is designed to implement one-to-one, life-to-life disciple-making in today's churches. Its instruction prepares participants for an inspiring journey of personal spiritual growth and ministry. Each weekly session will strengthen your usefulness in the Kingdom as you acquire new ministry skills. Because life-to-life training is now being emphasized in churches worldwide, you can look forward to both using and sharing everything you learn during this course's highly motivational instruction. Its interactive methodology produces new vision and provides spiritual training for a lifestyle of New Testament disciple-making.

A Personal Word from Billie Hanks Jr. –
Thank you for being a teammate in the Great Commission! You can begin this course by thinking about the following definition: Disciple-making refers to a healthy biblical relationship in which a more mature Christian spends quality time with a younger believer, showing him or her how to walk by faith, develop godly character, and gain proficiency in ministry skills. When personal training is combined with traditional small group teaching, highly accelerated spiritual growth takes place naturally, just as it did in the early Christian community.

It's important for you to first refine your own spiritual disciplines. Then you will be prepared to transfer those skills to others. The first few weeks of this instruction will focus on that preparation.

The life-to-life ministry of a Christian disciple-maker employs the biblical methodology of spiritual multiplication described in 2 Timothy 2:2. The apostle Paul wrote, *"And the things you have heard me say in the presence of many witnesses entrust to reliable people who will also be qualified to teach others."* The process of entrusting biblical teachings to others enables spiritual growth and personal witness to multiply naturally.

This course's mission is to help churches train disciple-makers to personally befriend and equip new church members with the needed spiritual skills to enjoy a lifetime of effective ministry.

Why New Testament Disciple-Making Is Vitally Important –

New believers deserve far more than a handshake when they join any Christian church. They need a Christ-centered friendship! This requires having believers who are prepared to walk with them while investing in their lives. Through such spiritual friendships, your church's new members will learn how to grow, use their spiritual gifts, and feel welcome in the church. To assist with this ministry, you will be equipped to personally disciple new members and help them develop a network of spiritually motivated Christian friends.

In addition to providing spiritual fellowship, you will answer new members' questions and become their personal prayer partner. Through this relational ministry, every person discipled will be encouraged to join a Bible-study group and faithfully participate in worship. This investment of time and spiritual influence is based on instructive verses like Proverbs 13:20a: *"He who walks with wise men will be wise..."* Experience has demonstrated that accelerated Christian growth takes place naturally in the context of a meaningful spiritual relationship with a more mature fellow believer.

PLANT YOUR STAND! FIND A WAY

Intentionality –

Many churches have no intentional process for personal training designed to successfully assimilate new members. Consequently, pastors are merely left to *hope* their church's new members will find dedicated Christians to disciple them. This frequent but often unrecognized omission leaves their "back doors" wide open! In contrast, many churches like yours are now providing a long-term disciple-making process because they want to welcome, encourage, and equip their new members. This is the underlying reason your pastor and church staff have adopted this life-changing course of instruction. Both the Scriptures and the concepts you'll receive will help you prepare future generations of disciple-makers for their ministries.

The Lord clearly revealed His deep personal concern about the special needs of new Christians. For example, He asked, *"Simon son of John, do you love me...?"* When Simon Peter answered, *"Yes, Lord"* the Lord replied, *"Tend my lambs."* (John 21:15) Our Good Shepherd made it perfectly clear that investing in new believers' lives unmistakably demonstrates our love for God.

Christian Witness –

For years, churches have overlooked their most valuable asset for fulfilling their assigned mission. Ironically, this neglected spiritual resource is their own membership's newest believers. Why are these fledgling Christians often so effective in terms of outreach? They are typically overflowing with inner joy and still share natural *relational bridges* with non-Christian family members and friends. Potentially, each one can learn to testify spontaneously. You will soon be walking alongside these new Christians, showing them how to respond to daily witnessing opportunities. Through your example, many will learn to share their faith as a lifestyle and learn how to personally encourage and equip others. This simple life-to-life discipling process is the way spiritual multiplication begins and grows in a healthy church environment.

New Insight –

Increasingly, today's pastors are realizing the importance of providing good examples for new church members to follow. Christian educators also acknowledge that although disciple-making has long been neglected, it's a vital part of a healthy church's ministry. In past decades, a wide variety of new-member classes have been conducted to help churches close their "back doors." However, it is generally acknowledged that our serious global-attrition problem still exists. This long-standing condition has confirmed that reliance on a small-group approach for effective new-member assimilation has proved inadequate. Extensive field testing in numerous countries has revealed that the most natural and successful method of new-member assimilation is simply Christ-centered friendships. This course focuses on the observable reasons a relational methodology has proved so reliable whenever it has been practiced through the centuries.

Friendship Factor – MEET PEOPLE

Studies show that feeling connected is highly important to new church members. They desire meaningful Christian friendships. Without those bonding relationships, over time, they tend to exit unnoticed through their churches' "back doors." This is one reason why *Becoming A Disciple-Maker* has been developed. It helps create a sustained environment of enjoyable fellowship. This warm spiritual atmosphere produces contentment and increased maturity. Because your ministry assignment is to provide immediate and long-term spiritual growth for new members, you will meet a strategic ministry need. Without your investment of time and encouragement, a significant percentage of your church's new believers and other new members will predictably fail to mature. As a result, many of them will never learn how to effectively share their faith. This simple but often repeated pattern of neglect is why so many new Christians gradually become discouraged and inactive. Looking back, few of them will ever comprehend why their church experience was so unfulfilling. They will live with mixed feelings of guilt and frustration, having once tasted the truth and liking it, but not learning to grow. Sadly, this failure describes the ongoing observable pattern of many new Christians worldwide.

Individual Care –

Because new Christians enter the Lord's churches as newborn believers, they must be treated like lambs. Through *Operation Multiplication's* relational ministry of personal follow-up, needed spiritual nurture is immediately available. Personal spiritual encouragement is provided until each new member is growing consistently, sharing his or her faith naturally, and successfully equipping others. The Bible describes this loving spirit of personalized care as it was first experienced in the early church. Paul wrote, *"We proved to be gentle among you, as a nursing mother tenderly cares for her own children."* (1 Thessalonians 2:7)

Freedom of Expression –

Through personal friendship, an environment of genuine openness steadily develops in disciple-making churches. As time passes, their patient, relational approach to new-member assimilation allows for sensitive subjects to be addressed. As needed, relational ministry provides the opportunity for life's predictable trials and challenges to be privately discussed in the light of scriptural teaching. As a result, positive spiritual progress typically takes place in the lives of those equipped. You will observe this growing new spiritual maturity as you meet with your trainees. The Bible summarizes this wonderful experience of transformation: *"Therefore if anyone is in Christ, he is a new creature; the old things passed away; behold, new things have come."* (2 Corinthians 5:17)

Spiritual Growth –

You will be prepared for your future ministry and function as a spiritual role model. Philippians 4:9 says, *"Whatever you have learned or received or heard from me, or seen in me—put it into practice, and the God of peace will be with you."* This verse inspires us to focus on our own spiritual development as we seek to be a good example to others. This spiritual apprenticeship process is based on the timeless biblical model described by King Solomon:

> *"Iron sharpens iron,*
> *So one man sharpens another."* (Proverbs 27:17)

Scripture's relational methodology is the dependable path to continued spiritual development. *Operation Multiplication's* life-to-life training follows that historical pattern. Its rewarding ministry helps equip new church members to *"...grow in the grace and knowledge of our Lord and Savior Jesus Christ. To Him be the glory, both now and to the day of eternity. Amen."* (2 Peter 3:18)

Flexible Schedule –

This course's customized format makes it easy to reschedule a meeting if you or your new member are unavoidably detained. Because of this flexibility, important instruction is never missed. Another secret behind the effectiveness of this equipping process is its focus on consistency. The weekly assignments provide for quality time to be spent together in prayer, Bible study, fellowship, and ministry-building activities. The Scriptures describe this relational aspect of the Lord's leadership style by reminding us that, *"And He appointed twelve, so that they would be with Him and that He could send them out to preach."* (Mark 3:14) His personal association with the Twelve was at the very core of His ministry.

Balanced Ministry –

Pause for a moment to visualize a magnificent grand piano. Next, ask yourself, Why does it have three legs? Would you agree that each leg performs an equally important physical function? Without each of its legs doing their part, the instrument would be unable to fulfill its musical purpose. Just as a grand piano needs all three of its legs, a church needs the use of all three of its New Testament methods of communication: *preaching, teaching,* and *training.* Today, most churches are blessed with good preaching and teaching, but few have a biblically based ministry of training. In many cases, this third New Testament feature of an effective ministry is either neglected or totally missing.

Spiritual Multiplication –

For a church's ministry to be robust and reach its full potential, the transition from *spiritual addition* to *spiritual multiplication* must take place. Multiplication is the powerful spiritual principle by which the church was called to carry out the Great Commission. *"Other seeds fell into the good soil, and as they grew up and increased, they yielded a crop and produced thirty, sixty, and a hundredfold."* (Mark 4:8) However, for this first-century methodology to experience church wide acceptance, our current generation of Christians must be helped to comprehend its importance. The world's spiritual harvest fields can only be reaped through our participation in personal disciple-making. When the Lord's highly committed church members faithfully apply this ministry pattern, over time, any city, state, or nation can be evangelized. The first-century church's example of disciple-making was so natural, transferable, and achievable that any contemporary congregation can experience it! This dynamic process simply requires an understanding of verses like 2 Timothy 2:2, plus the resolute decision to equip enough disciple-makers to individually equip every new church member to grow, share their faith, and multiply spiritually.

Closing the Church's "Back Door" – LIFEWAY REPORT

Many concerned Christian leaders are now analyzing the alarming attrition rate within their own denominations. Through their personal experience, they are acutely aware that today's new believers are facing a wide range of worldly temptations and distractions. They know the church's enemy can effectively prey on new members' primary areas of vulnerability to erode their spiritual vitality. The Lord's parable of the seed graphically illustrates this unchanging reality: *"Other seed fell among the thorns, and the thorns came up and choked it, and it yielded no crop."* (Mark 4:7) This also demonstrates how these negative spiritual influences can impact any Christian's personal walk and witness. Given these circumstances, our first line of responsibility is to carefully guide and protect all new believers.

A Worldwide Impact –

As Christianity restores the early church's long-neglected methodology of learning by observation, a dynamic new generation of witnesses is being prepared for service. Luke 10:2 tells us that *"The harvest is plentiful, but the workers are few."* Therefore, we are instructed to ask the Lord to, *"send out workers into His harvest field."* The global need for equipped workers has never been greater. Due to the sheer number of unreached people, Christians of every country are being led to rediscover how to make disciples and multiply spiritually. Your ministry is therefore greatly needed. May you catch the vision for a lifestyle of relational ministry and carry out your strategic personal role in fulfilling the Great Commission!

In that prayer,

Billie Hanks Jr.
Matthew 24:14

Randy Craig
Hebrews 12:1

Session One

Disciple-Making: An Overview

Discipleship & Disciple-Making

Most of us are familiar with the word *discipleship*, however, during this course we'll use the more relational term *disciple-making*.

Let's consider how these two related terms are currently being used in church life.

- *Discipleship* generally refers to traditional *Christian education*.
- *Disciple-Making* refers to the process of spiritual multiplication through one-to-one, life-to-life equipping relationships like Paul experienced with Timothy, Titus, and other growing believers.

The ministry objective of this course is to prepare successive generations of dedicated church members to invest their lives in fulfilling the Great Commission. The church's response to our Lord's mandate calls for the sustained development of dedicated Christians who will devote themselves to sharing their faith, making disciples, and multiplying spiritually. Our generation's challenge is to model that biblical lifestyle and set the right spiritual example.

For many Christians, the most intimidating aspect of discipleship is learning to share their personal witness. However, this doesn't have to be the case. As we develop *spiritual growth skills* and mature, witnessing simply becomes the *natural overflow* of our relationship with Christ.

Fulfilling your ministry potential primarily requires the willingness to develop spiritual discipline. For that reason Paul exhorted Timothy to, *"...discipline yourself for the purpose of godliness"* (1 Timothy 4:7) This lifestyle demands the earnest desire to continue growing toward maturity. It also requires a willingness to **MODEL** what you learn, passing those new ministry skills on to others. As this New Testament way of thinking becomes an established part of your life, your effectiveness as a Christian will steadily increase.

To better understand how we're intended to carry out the Great Commission, let's evaluate the major difference between participating in a normal short-term *church program* as opposed to establishing a consistent *disciple-making lifestyle*.

Church Programs: Growing churches normally offer a wide range of excellent ministry programs and events. However, most of them have a projected time for **CONCLUSION**.

Disciple-Making Lifestyle: Authentic New Testament disciple-making is a deeply fulfilling **APPROACH TO LIFE**. This exciting lifestyle is continually enriched by its *unending* new experiences in personal ministry. Through Christian love, expressed in the context of equipping relationships, fellow believers are progressively prepared to value and enjoy their spiritual growth. As this process transpires, they begin acquiring and passing on new *spiritual growth skills* from one spiritual generation to the next. This is how disciple-making took place and multiplied naturally in the early church.

Life-to-life equipping relationships help growing Christians develop spiritual growth skills like:
- Learning to *listen to God* with a yielded spirit
- Becoming consistent in our individual *daily quiet times*
- *Studying God's Word* for knowledge, character development, and Christian doctrine
- *Memorizing Scripture* for greater faith, purity, and wisdom
- *Meditating on Scripture* for inner peace and fellowship with God
- *Praying daily* for the opportunity to be the Lord's witness
- Becoming a life-long *Great Commission disciple-maker* who multiplies naturally.

Interactive life-to-life _TRAINING_ will be our primary focus throughout this course. However, the relational aspect of this instruction will not begin until the fourth week of study. By then, each one of us will have had sufficient time to select a ministry teammate from our group.

During this relational discipleship training, we'll each make steady weekly progress while practicing new ministry. In teams of two, we'll experience the time-tested spiritual disciplines being studied. This inspirational one-to-one instruction will take place outside our weekly group sessions. During these eight personal-training meetings, we'll utilize _Operation Multiplication's_ multiple generation disciple-making materials.

> _"...All authority has been given to Me in heaven and on earth. Go therefore and make disciples of all the nations, baptizing them in the name of the Father and the Son and the Holy Spirit..."_ (Matthew 28:18&19)

Great Commission

Disciple-making was unquestionably to be the church's core ministry. However, its essential life-to-life methodology, which was so normal to the Lord's first-century disciples was slowly lost and over time, almost completely forgotten. Today, however, this highly effective approach to ministry is being rediscovered and implemented in leading churches worldwide.

Spiritual Growth Assignment:

Carefully read the _Course Introduction_ starting on page ix of your _Becoming A Disciple-Maker Student's Guide_. As you review this foundational information, mark your personal insights for next week's discussion. You may wish to use a highlighter.

PREACHING
① 1 TO MANY

DISCIPLE-MAKING
* TRAINING ③ [HEALTHY CHURCH] ② TEACHING
1 X 1 1 TO SMALL GROUP

SESSION TWO

CHOOSING TO BE USABLE

[handwritten: CHRISTIANS FAIL BECAUSE TWO REASONS ① NO CLEAR PATH ② FREE WILL (CHOICE) LUKEWARM]

Spiritual Hunger *[handwritten: REV. 3:16]*

Jesus said, *"Blessed [or Happy] are those who hunger and thirst for righteousness, for they shall be satisfied."* (Matthew 5:6) Notice that the Lord described a believer's *spiritual hunger* as the means for finding *[handwritten: HAPPINESS]* and *[handwritten: SATISFACTION]* .

The Lord also explained the relationship of prayer to happiness when He said, *"Until now you have asked for nothing in My name; ask and you will receive, so that your joy may be made full."* (John 16:24)

Paul modeled this joyful positive attitude in spite of his many challenging situations. While a prisoner in a Philippian jail he wrote these encouraging words, *"Rejoice in the Lord always; again I will say, rejoice! –"Be anxious for nothing..." – "I have learned to be content in whatever circumstances I am." –"I can do all things through Him who strengthens me." – "And my God will supply all your needs according to His riches in glory in Christ Jesus"* (Philippians 4:4,6,11,13,19)

This universal sense of need exists because our creator uniquely *[handwritten: DESIGNED]* us with a natural spiritual hunger. Mankind instinctively *wants* to establish a relationship with Him. However, without Christ's indwelling presence, that inner hunger remains unsatisfied.

The Lord reminds us of this by saying, *"I am the bread of life. Whoever comes to me will never go hungry, and whoever believes in me will never be thirsty."* (John 6:35) To truly be content and satisfied, a growing Christian needs *continual spiritual nourishment*.

[handwritten: WE MUST BE T.]

Being Filled With God's Spirit

The Holy Spirit is the ~~power Source~~ that helps us live out the Christian life.

To seek the Lord's best for our lives, we must personally ~~CHOOSE~~ to be filled and controlled by His Spirit. The Bible says, *"And do not get drunk with wine, for that is dissipation, but be filled with the Spirit."* (Ephesians 5:18) This is God's spiritual plan for every born-again believer. Being filled with the Holy Spirit is a privilege that waits on our *daily decision to give Him total control of our lives.*

In summary, at the very moment you personally accept the Lord Jesus as your Savior, you are *baptized by His Spirit* into His spiritual body and become part of God's family. Then, as you continue releasing your grip, giving Him control over your life, you will be filled with His Spirit and empowered to live the Christian life!

The key to being filled and used by God is not in having another spiritual experience, but simply remaining hungry and totally *yielded – releasing your will to His.* 1 Corinthians 12:13 explains that our spiritual baptism takes place once at the moment of our spiritual rebirth. *"For by one Spirit we were all baptized into one body, whether Jews or Greeks, whether slaves or free, and we were all made to drink of one Spirit."* However, the Bible teaches that being filled is a daily, hourly, decision.

The Bible says, *"Do not quench the Spirit."* (1 Thessalonians 5:19) and this is illustrated by the squeezing of the sponge. *Lordship* means exactly what you might expect. Serving Christ best and enjoying life most comes when we continually seek and faithfully follow the Holy Spirit's guidance.

Spiritual power comes from being *controlled*, and being controlled comes as the result of being filled. Being *filled* is the result of the moment by-moment decision to live by faith – with a *yielded heart.*

When you're filled with God's Spirit, you become like a beautiful tree, producing the healthy fruit of *love, joy, peace, patience, kindness, goodness, faithfulness, gentleness, self-control* (Galatians 5:22-

23). Who wouldn't want that wonderful quality of life? Ironically, *our greatest strength comes from our greatest dependence*. Paul explained, *"I can do all things through Him who strengthens me."* (Philippians 4:13)

Spiritual Growth Produces Usability

Just as we anticipate physical growth when a baby is first born, God looks at our lives with a similar spiritual expectation. Our seasons of growth should steadily continue to please Him. This is why the Bible says, *"Grow in the grace and knowledge of our Lord and Savior Jesus Christ."* (2 Peter 3:18) and *"...be taken forward to maturity..."* (Hebrews 6:1)

It's spiritually HEALTHY to desire a deeper faith, and it's spiritually unhealthy to be satisfied with remaining as we are. The Bible calls us to ever-increasing usability, purity, and holiness: *"Do not conform to the pattern of this world, but be transformed by the renewing of your mind. Then you will be able to test and approve what God's will is— His good, pleasing and perfect will."* (Romans 12:2) 1 Peter 1:15&16 says, *"But just as He who called you is holy, so be holy in all you do; for it is written: "Be holy, because I am holy.""*

OUR CHOICE

Any sins we cling to and continually think about are the unmistakable evidence of our current areas of need. Our thoughts reveal exactly where our affections actually lie. The Bible says, *"As a man thinks within himself, so he is."* (Proverbs 23:7)

My THO

The object of Christian discipleship is personal OBEDIENCE to God, not just more knowledge about Him. Our goal is to APPLY what the Scriptures teach us about putting God's kingdom needs ahead of our own. When the Lord Jesus spoke about this priority He said, *"But seek first His kingdom and His righteousness, and all these things will be added to you."* (Matthew 6:33)

It is our love for God that inspires growing spiritual obedience. It produces mature Christian CHARACTER. Jesus emphasized this fact when He proclaimed, *"If you love me, keep my commands"* (John 14:15) *Our love for God is most dramatically revealed by one solitary attribute: our consistent daily passion to do His will.*

Toward Spiritual Maturity

For some Christians, spiritual growth has always seemed like an illusive mystery; however, it doesn't need to be that way. God will enable you to both please and serve Him if by faith you simply follow these spiritual steps covered during this course:

- Confess the known sins in your life and, with His help, determine to renounce them.
- Pray to be filled and controlled by the Holy Spirit as your normal way of life.
- Develop daily spiritual growth skills such as the "quiet time," Bible reading, Bible study, Scripture memorization, prayer, and personal meditation on the Word of God.
- Ask daily for the opportunity to serve as a Christian witness and Great Commission disciple-maker.

Spiritual Growth Assignment:

1. Spend some quality time alone with God asking Him to show you the specific areas of your life that need correction and spiritual development.

2. After reflection and sincere confession, ask Him to fill and control you with His Holy Spirit.

3. Read chapter 1, *The Vision for Spiritual Multiplication*, starting on page 99 of your *Becoming A Disciple-Maker Student's Guide*. Mark new insights and be prepared to share them with the group next week.

4 - Be Praying For My Timothy.

SESSION THREE

WHY
MAKE DISCIPLES?

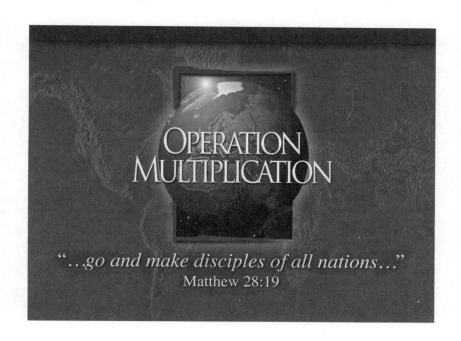

"*...go and make disciples of all nations...*"
Matthew 28:19

New believers are like
new born babies.
They need personal, spiritual care.

"But we proved to be gentle among you, as a nursing mother tenderly cares for her own children." (1 Thessalonians 2:7)

Looking for a friend at church

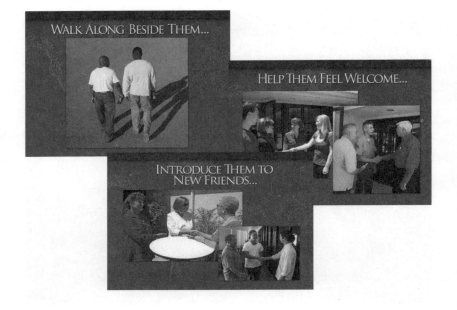

"For no one can lay a foundation other than the one which is laid, which is Jesus Christ." (1 Corinthians 3:11)

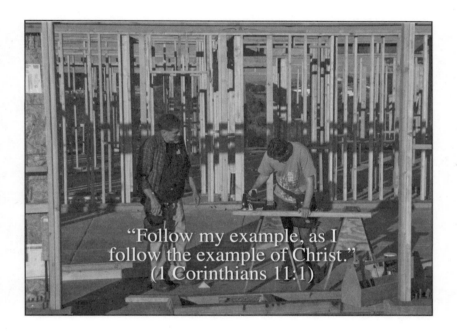

"Follow my example, as I
follow the example of Christ."
(1 Corinthians 11:1)

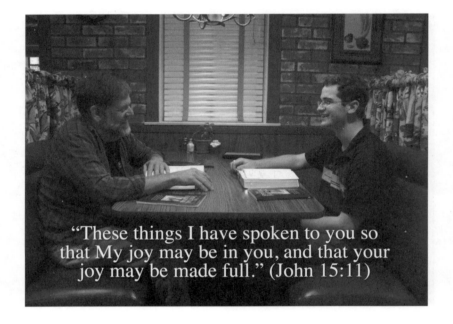

"These things I have spoken to you so that My joy may be in you, and that your joy may be made full." (John 15:11)

"Still other seed fell on good soil. It came up, grew and produced a crop, multiplying thirty, sixty, or even a hundred times."
(Mark 4:8)

Jesus said, "These are the ones on whom seed was sown on good soil and they hear the Word and accept it." (Mark 4:20)

"I planted, Apollos watered, but God caused the increase." (1 Corinthians 3:6)

Week 3

Week 4

Week 5

Week 6

Week 7

Week 6

Jesus said, "My Father is glorified by this, that you bear much fruit."
(John 15:8)

By the way…
what happened to our first tomato
plant which received personal
care from the very beginning?

After 14 weeks — it produced 52 tomatoes!

Jesus said, "Other seed fell on good soil. It came up, grew, and produced a crop, multiplying thirty, sixty, or even a hundred times". (Mark 4:8)

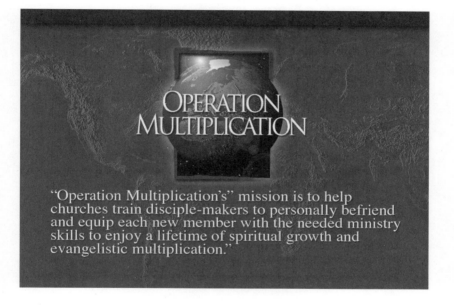

OPERATION MULTIPLICATION

"Operation Multiplication's" mission is to help churches train disciple-makers to personally befriend and equip each new member with the needed ministry skills to enjoy a lifetime of spiritual growth and evangelistic multiplication."

Spiritual Growth Assignment:

Read Chapter 2, *Disciple-Making and the Christian Church* starting on page 107 of your *Becoming A Disciple-Maker Student's Guide*. Mark highlights and arrive prepared to share them with the group next week.

SAM's MISSION

1. LOVE GOD

2. LOVE OTHERS

3. MAKE DISCIPLES
   THAT MAKE DISCIPLES

SESSION FOUR

HOW TO
MAKE DISCIPLES

During this session we're going to become better acquainted with our course materials so we can use them effectively in our ministries as disciple-makers.

Spiritual Growth Assignment:

This week marks an exciting step toward becoming a disciple-maker! For the next seven weeks, we will continue receiving *teaching* in our group, but we will now be adding one-to-one discipleship *training* in teams of two, so please follow these steps –

1. Pair up with a teammate in our group today (men with men and women with women).

2. We will continue meeting weekly as a group for instruction through *teaching* but then you will meet again one-to-one for personal *training* on another day of the week. This can be done over coffee or tea, during a meal, at any mutually convenient location. Usually only 1½ hours are needed.

3. Decide on a certain day, time, and place where you and your teammate will meet this week to complete Session One of *A Call to Joy.* Be sure to exchange phone numbers and e-mail addresses.

4. In preparation for completing Session One of *A Call to Joy*, both of you will prepare to be leaders using the *A Call to Joy Discipler's Guide.* During your one-to-one meeting, one of you will role play as the *Discipler* and the other as the *Timothy* using the *A Call to Joy Timothy's Guide.* When you complete 1/2 of the session, simply trade roles and finish the rest of the material.

5. Be sure to complete the Spiritual Growth Assignment and read the disciple-making chapter at the end of the *A Call to Joy* session. Mark highlights and discuss them with your teammate the following week.

SESSION FIVE

LEARNING TO LISTEN TO GOD

Internalizing God's Word

During the next few weeks, we will be exploring the benefits of several basic *spiritual growth skills*. The Lord said *"If you continue in My word, then you are truly disciples of Mine."* (John 8:31) This is why learning to establish a regular pattern of applying His teachings in our lives will be this week's primary spiritual focus.

Experience tells us there are no shortcuts to authentic Christian discipleship. It also teaches us that familiarity with Jesus' lifestyle and teachings is at the very heart of a successful Christian life. Developing the spiritual maturity which He desires for us requires time; self-discipline; and above all, the desire to *LISTEN* and *OBEY*.

Jesus said, *"Man shall not live on bread alone, but on every word that proceeds out of the mouth of God."* (Matthew 4:4) A disciple-making lifestyle takes root and grows when we apply our *FAITH* and act in obedience to what God says. Learning to internalize God's "bread of life" will help deepen your faith as you prepare for your personal role in completing the Great Commission.

"For the word of God is living and active and sharper than any two-edged sword, and piercing as far as the division of soul and spirit, of both joints and marrow, and able to judge the thoughts and intentions of the heart." (Hebrews 4:12)

Dawson Trotman, one of the 20th century's most experienced disciple-makers, often used this verse along with a transferable illustration

51

designed to encourage growing Christians. It helps the Lord's disciples evaluate their level of spiritual development. The key to this diagram's lasting effectiveness is its simplicity. Its graphic depiction of our upward journey toward maturity can easily be used in any culture or generation.

Our individual ministry progress is the result of *acting* on what the Holy Spirit teaches us, so let's focus on the needed spiritual growth skills for our personal development. The hand illustration presents six different ways to internalize the teachings of Scripture.

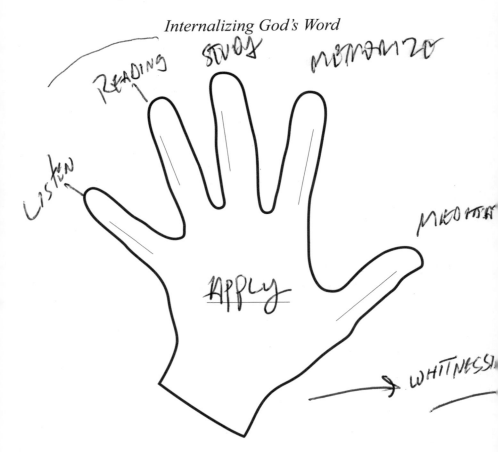

Internalizing God's Word

Listening to God's Word

Romans 10:17 explains that *"faith comes from hearing, and hearing by the word of Christ."* The Bible clearly teaches that hearing Scripture read or taught increases our faith.

The first skill we'll seek to fortify is intentionally *listening to the Holy Spirit*. We should regularly exercise this life-changing spiritual discipline during sermons, group Bible studies, and daily quiet times. This practice requires an open __ATTENTIVE____HEART__ during worship, plus concentration on the personal __APPLICATION__ of what we are being taught.

People usually begin changing the way they listen when they genuinely desire to grow. When this occurs, a believer's attitude and behavior will positively be transformed. In terms of usability, every Christian's __WILL__ is always involved. Therefore, the real question is, are you genuinely ready to subordinate your will to His? This is where growing faith predictably leads us.

In Matthew 11:15 and *seven* additional places in the Gospels, Jesus says, *"He who has ears to hear, let him hear."*

Our objective during this training is to develop highly sensitive spiritual ears that truly yearn to hear God's truth. Our goal will be to emulate the Israelites of Ezra's day when God's Word was read to them:

"Then Ezra the priest brought the law before the assembly of men, women, and all who could listen with understanding...he read from it...from early morning until midday...and all the people were attentive... when he opened it, all the people stood up. Then Ezra blessed the Lord the great God. And all the people answered, "Amen, Amen!" while lifting up their hands; then they bowed low and worshiped the Lord with their faces to the ground." (Nehemiah 8:2-6)

When we participate in a worship service or a Bible study, Satan doesn't want us to arrive relaxed and prepared to listen. Instead, he wants us to arrive too late, too upset, or too mentally preoccupied to recognize and follow the Holy Spirit's leading. The enemy wins every time our thoughts become divided and are distracted during worship.

It is wise for us to realize that both in the Old Testament and the New Testament, the emphasis was upon Scripture, so God's Word was always read and explained.

Maintaining a focused, __TEACHABLE__ attitude should be one of our lifelong pursuits. This victory typically derives from seeking God's leadership with a pre-determined will to obey. Our attitude and acts of obedience are the form of worship that show God we love Him.

Retaining God's Word
So far, we've focused on how to become spiritually prepared by learning how to *listen*. Now let's consider being physically prepared to retain what the Holy Spirit teaches us. With this objective in mind, let's shift our focus to our *Spiritual Journals*.

A *Spiritual Journal* is a devotional tool designed to help me – __ORGANIZE__ and __RETAIN__ what the Holy Spirit teaches me daily.

The Holy Spirit's Ministry
It might help you to think of the Holy Spirit much as you would a highly honored professor. Because you're a believer, the Holy Spirit resides in your heart as your teacher. The Bible explains that... *"His anointing teaches you about all things, and is true..."* (1 John 2:27)

Every hour consciously spent in the awareness of God, the Holy Spirit's presence is a source of personal blessing. Remember His invitation: *"Cease striving and know that I am God..."* (Psalm 46:10) He gives us inner peace, conviction, and instruction. Our special private, daily fellowship with God can be enjoyed almost anytime. However, being alone with Him at the beginning of the day is closest to our Lord's example.

Taking notes in our *Spiritual Journals* will help us retain fresh insights from sermons and Bible studies. As we effectively internalize God's Word, we steadily become more usable disciples.

Spiritual Pearls
Jesus said, *"Do not give that what is holy to dogs, and do not throw your pearls before swine."* (Matthew 7:6) In that same spirit, our

Lord doesn't give His spiritual pearls to those who are unprepared to __Recognize__ or __Value__ them. That's why He spoke in parables.

Are you ready to say *"Yes"* to God by faith, even before He speaks to you? Remember that your personal __Obedience__ is closely equated with the degree of trust you have in Him. This is why it's important to learn to immediately respond to The Holy Spirit's leading. By faith as His disciple, you must stay perpetually prepared to say *"Yes"* whenever He calls. Reflect for a minute on the experience of His first disciples. They immediately responded, and that obedience helped mark them for future leadership. Jesus said to Peter and Andrew, *"Follow Me, and I will make you fishers of men. Immediately they left their nets and followed Him."* (Matthew 4:19-20)

Spiritual Growth Assignment:

1. Before next week's group meeting, enjoy your next one-to-one *A Call to Joy* training session with your teammate. In preparation for completing Session Two of *A Call to Joy*, both of you will prepare to be leaders using the *A Call to Joy Discipler Guide*. During your one-to-one meeting, one of you will role play as the *Discipler* and the other as the *Timothy* using the *A Call to Joy Timothy's Guide*. When you complete 1/2 of the session, simply trade roles and finish the rest of the material.

2. Be sure to complete the *Spiritual Growth Assignment* and read the disciple-making chapter at the end of the *A Call to Joy* session. Mark highlights and discuss them with your teammate the following week.

3. Read pages 2–3 in *The Spiritual Journal*. Mark your insights and be prepared to discuss them during next week's group meeting.

A DADOR GOD

C ONFESS SINS

T HANKSGIVING

S

SESSION SIX

READING
GOD'S WORD

Reading God's Word

The Lord Himself will faithfully teach you during your quiet times as you read His Word, so don't take this spiritual opportunity for granted. Following Jesus' resurrection, two perplexed believers were traveling on the road to Emmaus. Our risen Lord joined them and taught them as they walked. Later they exclaimed, *"Were not our hearts burning within us while He was speaking to us on the road, while He was explaining the Scriptures to us?"* (Luke 24:32)

Through the Holy Spirit's ministry, the Lord still opens the Scriptures to us in the same way today. The amazing reality is that because He indwells us, He still communicates with us just as naturally now as He did 20 centuries ago.

Jesus enables us to enjoy the same abundant life in the 21st century that He provided for His disciples in the first century. As we experience God's presence, our spirits soar and we increasingly learn to value what matters to Him. Remember that life's highest privilege is to serve Him. As His ambassadors, we're to live in the world but carefully **AVOID** being like it. The Bible says, *"And do not be conformed to this world, but be transformed by the renewing of your mind, so that you may prove what the will of God is, that which is good and acceptable and perfect."* (Romans 12:2) Reading God's Word and meditating on its instructions each morning are spiritual disciplines that enable us to receive His guidance and to engage in effective Christian service.

Think about the timeless wisdom contained in this Old Testament passage: *"Cease striving and know that I am God..."* (Psalm 46:10) It's usually when we're calm and quiet that the Lord shows us His plans and increases our understanding.

The Bible says, *"God Is faithful, through whom you were called into fellowship with His Son, Jesus Christ our Lord."* (1 Corinthians 1:9) Paul explained that we're individually called into close fellowship with our Lord. Unquestionably, this spiritual relationship is an undeserved honor which we could never deserve.

The apostle John explained, *"...Indeed our fellowship is with the Father, and with His Son Jesus Christ."* (1 John 1:3) To enjoy daily communion with Him, we must plan ahead and set aside quality time to be alone with Him. As one devoted Christian expressed it, "We each need to carve islands in our day solely to be quiet in His presence."

The Daily Quiet Time

The best part of the day to reserve for fellowship with the Lord is in the morning. David said, *"In the morning, O Lord, You will hear my voice. In the morning I will direct my prayers to You and eagerly watch."* (Psalm 5:3) It's exciting to be with Him and receive His peace and confidence for each new day!

His Word is like a light for us. The Bible says, *"Your Word is a lamp to my feet and a light to my path."* (Psalm 119:105) Additionally, the Bible is our primary source of spiritual nourishment, our daily bread. *"Give us this day our daily bread."* (Matthew 6:11) This is why we're instructed to enjoy it *daily*. As events take place in our lives, we eventually discover why we needed exactly what He taught us earlier during our quiet time. Each time this happens, our faith grows and our hearts overflow with appreciation and praise.

Look for gold nuggets

Obedience Requires Understanding

Just as a soldier carefully reviews his orders before going into battle, daily Bible reading gives us that same benefit. It provides God's guidance – *"...I will counsel you with My eye upon you."* (Psalm 32:8) Practically speaking, when a soldier unwisely chooses to engage in battle without reading his orders, he places himself in serious danger.

Such a careless attitude is sheer presumption. For a believer, living without God's guidance amounts to asking for defeat.

This is why it's always important to make your quiet time the first priority of your morning. You can do this while drinking coffee or enjoying hot tea. The point is to be awake and ready to experience relaxed personal fellowship with the Lord. If you wait until later in the day and try to fit your quiet time into an already busy schedule, you probably will not be successful in having one.

Without fail before takeoff, every responsible pilot _COMMUNICATES_ with his area's control tower. Your daily quiet time is exactly the same. The spiritual success of your day totally depends on living under the Holy Spirit's control and far-seeing guidance. He will provide daily spiritual direction each morning as you spend time alone with Him. The New Testament explains this dynamic invitation: *"Draw near to God and He will draw near to you..."* (James 4:8)

Lets' examine a related principle. Through your daily quiet times, God will give you continued inspiration and additional knowledge. However, this process of spiritual growth usually takes place slowly.

Without renewing our spiritual strength, every attempt we make in Christian ministry is an exercise in mediocrity. Remember, we can either pray for God's strength in the _MORNING_ or find ourselves needing to ask for His forgiveness at _NIGHT_. Our need for spiritual strength explains why a daily quiet time is essential for successful Christian living. In His humanity, the Lord Himself was our perfect example. The Bible says, *"In the early morning, while it was still dark, Jesus got up, left the house, and went away to a secluded place, and was praying there."* (Mark 1:35)

The day before, Jesus had been extremely busy. He had —
• preached in Capernaum
• delivered a man possessed by demons
• healed Peter's sick mother-in-law and
• ministered to a large crowd in which many were spiritually or physically ill.

Jesus said, *"The words that I speak to you I do not speak on My own authority; but the Father who dwells in Me does the works."* (John 14:10b) Our strength, like His, comes from obedience and dependence rather than from self assurance or human ability.

As busy and tired as the Lord had been, He still awakened early the next morning and spent time alone with His Father. When we follow Jesus' pattern of dependence on prayer, our strength is also renewed. He literally set the example for us. His devotional practice demonstrated the secret behind all spiritual growth.

In our Christian lives, unfortunately, a high percentage of us still eat only one or two spiritual meals each week – usually a Sunday worship service and a small-group Bible study. That's not nearly enough nourishment to sustain a growing disciple for a week. There was a reason the Lord taught us to pray, *"Give us this day our daily bread."* (Matthew 6:11) instead of our weekly bread. Our personal effectiveness requires a steady supply of renewed spiritual energy. → DON'T GIVE UP

The sad truth is that a large number of contemporary church members seldom read the Bible personally. They primarily pick it up only when they're in trouble and looking for comfort rather than daily nourishment and strength. Spiritually, this failure leaves them running on empty most of the time.

With that sobering thought on our minds, let's dedicate ourselves to pursuing a new, higher standard of excellence. We need to enjoy and model devotional consistency so each new spiritual generation will have a strong example to follow. This can be accomplished by faithfully reading the Bible every morning.

Our daily quiet time mustn't be perceived as an optional spiritual discipline. Instead, it must be viewed as an essential pre-requisite for continued growth and effective ministry.

Remember, the only way to mature spiritually is to, *"...discipline yourself for the purpose of godliness."* (1 Timothy 4:7) Athletes are only successful when they discipline themselves on a daily basis. The Bible says, *"Run in such a way that you may win."* (1 Corinthians 9:24)

Spiritual Growth Assignment:

1. Meet with your training teammate this week and complete the next session of *A Call to Joy*. In preparation for completing Session Three of *A Call to Joy*, both of you will prepare to be leaders using the *A Call to Joy Discipler's Guide*. During your one-to-one meeting, one of you will role play as the *Discipler* and the other as the *Timothy* using the *A Call to Joy Timothy's Guide*. When you complete 1/2 of the session, simply trade roles and finish the rest of the material.

2. Be sure to complete the *Spiritual Growth Assignment* and read the disciple-making chapter at the end of the *A Call to Joy* session. Mark highlights and discuss them with your teammate the following week.

SESSION SEVEN

STUDYING GOD'S WORD

Searching the Scriptures

The Apostle Paul complimented the new believers who lived in the city of Berea saying they *"...were more noble-minded...for they received the word with great eagerness, examining the Scriptures daily..."* (Acts 17:11)

Paul writes, *"Be diligent to present yourself approved to God as a workman who does not need to be ashamed, accurately handling the word of truth."* (2 Timothy 2:15) Peter adds, *"...sanctify Christ as Lord in your hearts, always being ready to make a defense to everyone who asks you to give an account for the hope that is in you, yet with gentleness and reverence."* (1 Peter 3:15) Both Paul and Peter encouraged Christians to study the Bible.

"If you continue in My word, then you are truly disciples of Mine"
(John 8:31)

Someone once wisely said, "A daily quiet time will point your ship in the right direction, but Bible study will put a steady wind in your sails!"

The Availability of Scripture

Many of us take owning Bibles for granted, and we don't comprehend the great privilege of having God's Word for personal study. However, if we had lived in the first century, we might have had to walk or ride for many miles to hear an apostle or another early church leader teach

63

from the Scriptures. Very few people had access to the limited number of handwritten manuscripts that existed.

In contrast, today, entire nations have easy access to God's Word. With such a privilege currently available, it's perplexing to observe the extent of biblical illiteracy that still exists, even among professing Christians. Owning a Bible isn't enough. The key is being dedicated enough to study it.

Becoming Useful

To become more effective in God's kingdom, we need to ask ourselves some honest questions.

- Do I really want God's best for my life?
- Am I tired of being lukewarm?
- Do I genuinely want to grow?
- Is my passion to influence the world for Christ?

If your answer is yes to any of these questions, Bible study is the next step on your journey. Always remember that the Holy Spirit is far more interested in shaping your _____ than in supplying your mind with additional information, so that is the real reason we study.

Preparation Steps

1. Prayerfully ask the Lord to give you understanding each time you read.
2. Submit your will to His will and ask Him to change you from within.
3. Use a modern translation with easily readable print.
4. Select convenient times during the week for personal Bible study.

You may be led to do your Bible study at night in preference to watching television or instead of other activities. After you've selected the most practical times of the day or night for study, think about those occasions much like making an appointment with a highly respected world leader. In reality, quality time spent alone with God is far more important than any other meeting you will ever attend.

Your personal Bible-study goals are to gain Scriptural _____ and _____ and then _____ those life-changing discoveries in your life. During your Bible studies, you look deeply into the Scriptures and slowly develop doctrinal understanding. Your quiet time is much like an appetizer, but Bible study provides a full meal.

Studying God's Word should never be viewed as an optional discipline. If you're serious about wanting to grow spiritually, you'll need to make this skill a lifelong personal discipline. Remember, Paul said, *"...discipline yourself for the purpose of godliness."* (1 Timothy 4:7) Learning how to study the Bible is a major step in that direction.

Your commitment to the spiritual discipline of personal Bible study will help determine how effective you become as a Christian disciple. Spending 30 to 60 minutes in study on selected days or nights is a good way to get started. If you have children, you can enjoy studying after they're asleep. Be intentional about Bible study and choose to build your life around the truths which you discover in Scripture.

Four Bible-Study Methods

1. **Word Study.** If your Bible has a concordance (an alphabetical listing of key words usually found on its back pages), you can—
   - select a word to study;
   - find passages where it appears;
   - thoughtfully read those verses;
   - discover ways the word is used;
   - write down your new insights;
   - prayerfully apply what you've learned.

If your Bible doesn't have a concordance, you can purchase a separate exhaustive concordance that provides the listing and location of every word used in the Bible. This inexpensive study aid will be a great asset for several Bible-study methods.

2. **Commentary Study.** Owning a Bible-commentary series written by a respected Christian author is like having your own personal teacher sitting with you as you study. Simply read the instruction about each chapter and then write down your favorite insights and personal applications. You can do this in the margins of your Bible or

in a separate Bible-study notebook. Next, thoughtfully consider each new discovery with practical application in mind.

With several million books in print, Warren Wiersbe's *Be Series* is a recommended set of commentaries for English-speaking Bible students. His plan of study leads readers through every book of the Bible. (See the Resource Section on page 113 of your *Becoming a Disciple-Maker Student's Guide.*) Additionally, good study Bibles are also available which contain helpful notes and background information on each page.

3. **Topical Study**. Use a concordance or, if available in your language, *Nave's Topical Bible* for this method of study. Collect and compare the available passages on any selected subject. Then meditate on the spiritual lessons being taught on that topic.

4. **Character Study**. Select any interesting biblical character and research the verses written about his or her life. Your spiritual objective will be to learn everything possible from that person's life experiences. Be prepared to take notes as you consider their faith, attitudes, strengths, and weaknesses. Then from each study, prayerfully seek to apply the knowledge gained. This will deepen your own life and ministry.

Word Study

As an example, let's complete a brief word study on the subject of *faith*. Using a concordance, we easily find more than 60 biblical references to our selected word. Of that number, Twenty-two references will refer to the fact that we're redeemed through faith in Jesus Christ.

"Now faith is the assurance of things hoped for, the conviction of things not seen." (Hebrews 11:1)

- Faith is *required* for salvation:
  "Therefore, having been justified by faith, we have peace with God through our Lord Jesus Christ, through whom also we have obtained our introduction by faith into this grace in which we stand; and we exult in hope of the glory of God." (Romans 5:1-2)

- God is *pleased* when we step out in faith:
  "And without faith it is impossible to please Him, for he who comes to God must believe that He is and that He is a rewarder of those who seek Him." (Hebrews 11:6)

- Our faith can be a *testimony*:
  "First, I thank my God through Jesus Christ for you all, because your faith is being proclaimed throughout the whole world." (Romans 1:8)

- Our faith is *increased by hearing the Scriptures* explained:
  "So faith comes from hearing, and hearing by the word of Christ." (Romans 10:17)

- Faith is to be the *central core* of our lives:
  "...whatever is not from faith is sin." (Romans 14:23)

- By faith we can *overcome selfish desires* and allow Christ to live through us:
  "I have been crucified with Christ; and it is no longer I who live, but Christ lives in me; and the life which I now live in the flesh I live by faith in the Son of God, who loved me and gave Himself up for me." (Galatians 2:20)

- We can help *strengthen a fellow believer's faith*:
  "...we sent Timothy, our brother and God's fellow worker in the gospel of Christ, to strengthen and encourage you as to your faith." (1 Thessalonians 3:2)

- The testing of our faith produces *endurance* and *maturity*:
  "Consider it all joy, my brethren, when you encounter various trials, knowing that the testing of your faith produces endurance. And let endurance have its perfect result, so that you may be perfect and complete, lacking in nothing." (James 1:2-4)

- Faith is required for effective prayer:
  "...ask in faith without any doubting..." (James 1:6)

- Authentic faith results in *Christian action*:
  "...faith, if it has no works, is dead, being by itself." (James 2:17)

"The mark of effective Bible study is not knowledge that 'puffs us up,' but love that 'builds us up.'" – Warren Wiersbe

"The Scriptures are both shallow enough for children to safely enter without fear and deep enough for theologians to swim without ever touching the bottom." – Warren Wiersbe

Suggestions for Success

- Remember that in good Bible study, *speed must never be your goal.*
- Always make *application* your personal spiritual objective.
- Watch out for this temptation: "I'm doing so well this week that I don't have a need for Bible study."
- Avoid slipping into the habit of immediately thinking, "Jim should read this" or perhaps, "This is just what our church needs." Instead, always apply your new Bible study insights to _____ first. Then, as the Lord leads you, share those new insights as often as needed.
- Don't forget that your _____ _____ at the beginning of each day is primarily for fellowship with God and His guidance. In contrast, focus your Bible studies on gaining additional knowledge and wisdom, for personal application.

Spiritual Growth Assignment

1. Using a concordance, conduct a brief word study and be ready to share your biblical insights and personal applications with the group next week.

2. Meet with your discipler teammate this week and complete the next session of *A Call to Joy*. In preparation for completing Session Four of *A Call to Joy*, both of you will prepare to be leaders using the *A Call to Joy Discipler Guide*. During your one-to-one meeting, one of you will role play as the *Discipler* and the other as the *Timothy* using the *A Call to Joy Timothy's Guide*. When you complete 1/2 of the session, simply trade roles and finish the rest of the material.

3. Be sure to complete the *Spiritual Growth Assignment* and read the disciple-making chapter at the end of the *A Call to Joy* session. Mark highlights and discuss them with your teammate the following week.

SESSION EIGHT

MEMORIZING MEDITATING, AND APPLYING GOD'S WORD

Memorizing God's Word

"These words, which I am commanding you today, shall be on your heart. You shall teach them diligently to your sons and shall talk of them when you sit in your house and when you walk by the way and when you lie down and when you rise up." (Deuteronomy 6:6-7)

From the earliest days, many centuries before the Bible was ever printed, God commanded His people to hide His Word in their hearts. Scripture was to be at the center of a believing family's life and a vital part of each person's experience.

The Lord Himself is our best example of Scripture memorization (see Matthew 4:1-11). Throughout His ministry, He demonstrated a great familiarity with the Torah, or what Christians refer to as the Old Testament. Jesus made more than 60 specific references to Old Testament verses in the four Gospels and consistently quoted them from memory.

Merely learning to say a verse from memory isn't a worthy spiritual objective. The real goal of Scripture memorization is to _____ with a verse long enough for its truth to saturate your soul and transform your values. Then it will affect the way you think and act. The verses you hide in your heart will remain with you like close lifelong friends.

Why Memorize Scripture?

Knowing Scripture has the following benefits. It will:

1. Increase your _____. The more Scripture you commit to memory, the easier it will be for the Holy Spirit

to guide, protect, and use you throughout your lifetime. Knowing God's Word is the clearest and easiest way to be guided. God's Word promises:

"I will instruct you and teach you in the way which you should go; I will counsel you with My eye upon you." (Psalm 32:8)

2. Help you overcome _____ as you pray and place your trust in God's promises. We're instructed to:

"Be anxious for nothing, but in everything by prayer and supplication with thanksgiving let your requests be made known to God." (Philippians 4:6)

3. Enables you to recognize and resist _____. The psalmist wrote:

"Your word I have treasured in my heart, that I may not sin against You." (Psalm 119:11)

4. Reminds you of the _____ of spiritual disobedience. Consider this warning:

"Do not be deceived, God is not mocked; for whatever a man sows, this he will also reap" (Galatians 6:7)

5. Equips you to confidently _____ the gospel with others. Peter said:

"Sanctify Christ as Lord in your hearts, always being ready to make a defense to everyone who asks you to give an account for the hope that is in you, yet with gentleness and reverence." (1 Peter 3:15)

6. Channels your _____ in a positive direction:

"Let your eyes look directly ahead and let your gaze be fixed straight in front of you." (Proverbs 4:25)

7. Provides spiritual insight for making wise daily _____. Think about this description of Scripture:

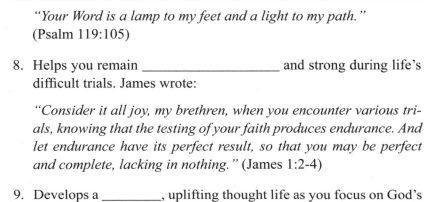

"Your Word is a lamp to my feet and a light to my path." (Psalm 119:105)

8. Helps you remain _____ and strong during life's difficult trials. James wrote:

    "Consider it all joy, my brethren, when you encounter various trials, knowing that the testing of your faith produces endurance. And let endurance have its perfect result, so that you may be perfect and complete, lacking in nothing." (James 1:2-4)

9. Develops a _____, uplifting thought life as you focus on God's Word. Paul wrote:

    "Finally, brethren, whatever is true, whatever is honorable, whatever is right, whatever is pure, whatever is lovely, whatever is of good repute, if there is any excellence and if anything is worthy of praise, dwell on these things." (Philippians 4:8)

Helpful Hints for Memorizing Scripture

1. Carry a Scripture-memory packet and use it to help you review your new verses.

2. Use your mealtimes with family members or friends to review each new weekly memory verse.

3. Repeat the reference before and after each verse as you review.

4. Meditate on the spiritual meaning of each new memory verse.

5. Be consistent in review.

6. Seek to memorize each week's new verse perfectly to improve your retention and provide confidence when quoting it.

7. Consider each new verse's biblical context by reading immediately before and after the words you're memorizing. Through this practice, you'll gain a better understanding of each verse's intended meaning.

8. Begin by simply repeating phrases from each new verse aloud as you memorize.

9. Next, concentrate on verbally emphasizing a few key words in each phrase until each verse is completely learned.

   "I can do all things through Christ who strengthens me." (Philippians 4:13)

10. Select your favorite translation for memorization.

11. Memorize Scripture with a friend and encourage one another to develop this life-long spiritual discipline. Remember that your ultimate goal is to live by the new truths which you hide in your heart.

Meditating on God's Word

"I will meditate on Your precepts and regard Your ways. I shall delight in Your statutes; I will not forget Your word." (Psalm 119:15-16)

Christian meditation is the discipline of prayerfully contemplating God's revelation of Himself as well as His inspired teachings – the Bible. This discipline helps us to learn how to listen to the Holy Spirit and deepen our relationship with Jesus Christ.

"Consider what I say, for the Lord will give you understanding in everything." (2 Timothy 2:7)

1. Choose memory verses that you desire to keep with you for a lifetime. (There's an excellent list of suggested verses on the back inside cover of your *Spiritual Journal*.)
2. Start by slowly reading and re-reading the verse you select.
3. Focus your attention on one phrase at a time as you consider its meaning. Next, prayerfully think about how to respond to what God is saying in each verse.

Example:

"Now may the God of hope fill you with all joy and peace in believing, so that you will abound in hope by the power of the Holy Spirit." (Romans 15:13)

- Lord, You are the essence of our hope.
- Without You there can be absolutely no hope.

- No matter what my circumstances may be, I can experience joy and peace through my faith in You.
- When I trust in what You say, You enable my life to overflow and became a natural witness to others.
- How is this victorious lifestyle made possible? Not through my human efforts, but by the power of Your Holy Spirit.

Because meditation is the apex of all spiritual disciplines, it requires the most time for quiet concentration. Even more importantly, it calls for the deeply sincere desire to discover and then _____ the Holy Spirit's leading.

Application

Application is the key to success with every spiritual discipline. Remember, James 1:22 says, *"But prove yourselves doers of the word, and not merely hearers who delude themselves."*

Spiritual Growth Assignment:

1. Meet with your teammate before next week's group meeting and complete the next session of *A Call to Joy*. In preparation for completing Session Five of *A Call to Joy*, both of you will prepare to be leaders using the *A Call to Joy Discipler's Guide*. During your one-to-one meeting, one of you will role play as the *Discipler* and the other as the *Timothy* using the *A Call to Joy Timothy's Guide*. When you complete 1/2 of the session, simply trade roles and finish the rest of the material.

2. Be sure to complete the *Spiritual Growth Assignment* and read the disciple-making chapter at the end of the *A Call to Joy* session. Mark highlights and discuss them with your teammate the following week.

Discipleship — Traditional Education
— Sunday School.
vs.
Disciple-making
↳ 1×1
Teaching
Train the Trainer

SESSION NINE

JESUS' METHOD OF DISCIPLE-MAKING

Jesus' Ministry Strategy

First let's consider three major truths.

1. The Lord Jesus is, was, and always will be God's eternal Son.
2. Being fully God and fully man, our Lord was the wisest person who ever lived.
3. Because of His divine wisdom, He knew exactly how to invest His life in the most effective manner. Expressed another way, if there had been a better way to accomplish His spiritual mission, He would have known what it was and could have used it.

By studying the Lord's actions and His use of time, we can better understand how to implement His equipping methodology. When we follow His pattern of relational disciple-making, spiritual multiplication can take place naturally during our lifetime!

First – It takes a ___DISCIPLE___ to make a ___DISCIPLE___.

Second – You need only a ___SHORT___ head start.

Jesus was definitely the greatest disciple-maker the world has ever seen. He demonstrated His relational training methodology by the way He lived. His original twelve disciples were equipped for their ministries primarily by *spending quality time with Him*. They were privileged to personally *observe* His sinless character, dependence on His Father, and highly effective ministry skills. Through this process, they learned how to become strong, godly, multiplying disciples themselves.

75

Third –We must serve the Lord with an awareness that our allotted time for ministry is at best – brief.

Unlike us, Jesus clearly knew precisely how long His life would last. Knowing this, He carefully invested His time in showing believers exactly how He wanted us to minister. He *modeled* disciple-making by showing us how to provide life-to-life training to each new spiritual generation of growing new believers.

Everything Jesus did was designed to produce positive spiritual results. Knowing His time was limited, He strategically utilized the world's best methodology to prepare future leaders to serve in His kingdom. Following His pattern, they were privileged to begin building His church.

Jesus' Ministry

- His confidence was initially placed in __12__ men.
- His strategy was to do a lasting work in the lives of a __FEW__ faithful followers who would multiply.
- His goal was to __REPRODUCE__ His divine life, values, and resources in the lives of those sincere believers who would give their lives to Him.

Jesus invested His maximum time equipping those who would bear the maximum responsibility for ministry in the spiritual life of His church.

By modeling this methodology daily, He personally demonstrated the timeless truth that spiritual __QUALITY__ multiplies naturally producing great __QUANTITY__.

Jesus left us a vivid example, and through it He showed us His timeless plan for fulfilling the Great Commission. He said, *"Truly, truly, I say to you, he who believes in Me, the works that I do, he will do also; and greater works than these he will do; because I go to the Father."* (John 14:12)

In public, Jesus carried out a very active ministry that included the following tasks.

- Preaching

- Teaching
- Healing
- Miracles

However, in private, the Lord equipped _future leaders_.
They learned how to *grow in character*, *share their faith*, *make disciples*, and *multiply spiritually*.

When Jesus ministered publicly in Israel, He preached to thousands, taught small groups, healed the blind, deaf, mute, lame, crippled, lepers, and paralytics. When He restored withered hands and removed fever, it became obvious that no disease was beyond His healing power. He also cast out demons, turned water into wine, walked on water, calmed turbulent seas, miraculously fed thousands, raised the dead, and personally rose from the grave. No one in world history has ever approached His combined attributes of love, power, justice, and mercy.

Jesus' public ministry was utterly astonishing! Yet in spite of all He said and did in the full sight of multitudes, His most enduring and far-reaching ministry took place _privately_. This was conducted almost unnoticed as He went about His daily activities. Through it, He succeeded in equipping and leaving behind 11 totally transformed men who would alter the course of world history. He equipped these humble men to serve as the future leaders of His church. Their training took place during the brief time they spent with Him in every conceivable ministry situation. *Observation* was the key. *"And He appointed twelve, so that they would be with Him and that He could send them out to preach..."* (Mark 3:14)

If Jesus had publicly healed all those who were sick in Galilee, taught the faithful, proclaimed the truth to multitudes and performed the world's greatest miracles but hadn't privately equipped highly dependable disciples, the Christian church we know and love wouldn't exist today.

It was the Lord's divine plan to call and leave behind a team of well-equipped disciples. They would be prepared to follow His example and successfully carry out the Great Commission. They would be

committed to both *teaching* and *training* each new spiritual generation of dedicated, growing believers. These multiplying first-century
Christians were ordinary people just like us and the Lord empowered
and instructed them to evangelize their generation. His command was
clear: *"Go therefore and make disciples of all the nations."* (Matthew
28:19)

Listening = Teaching
Watching = Training

- *Teaching* was Jesus' methodology for transferring spiritual
  __concepts__ and __values__.
- *Training* was Jesus' methodology for transferring effective
  __ministry skills__.

The apostles received the benefit of repeatedly seeing *both* of these
spiritual disciplines actually modeled as the Lord personally practiced
them.

Part of the time Jesus' early disciples simply sat and *listened* to Him.

On many other occasions they learned by *watching* Him.

Paul challenged the believers in Philippi to utilize both of the Lord's
fully proven methods. Let's read the first phrase of this next verse in
unison: *"Whatever you have learned or received or __heard__ from me ..."*

Now let's read the second phrase,
"... or __seen__ in me – put it into practice. ..."

"...and the God of peace will be with you." (Philippians 4:9)

Life-to-life training is based on the principle of __OBSERVATION__.
This principle is vital to the spiritual development of each new generation of Christians. For that reason, Paul gave us this timeless instruction: *"Be imitators of me, just as I also am of Christ."* (1 Corinthians
11:1)

Before the Lord sent the apostles out to serve as His ambassadors
and witnesses, He first *equipped* them for their mission. That needed
protocol remains unchanged today. New believers must be *personally
equipped* for service in the Lord's church world-wide.

The disciples' basic training took place during their close _Association_ ✓
with Jesus. Remember, the Bible records, *"He appointed twelve, so that they would be with Him and that He could send them out to preach."* (Mark 3:14)

During the Lord's brief but world-impacting life, He utilized three different but highly complementary methods of communication:
* One-to-one = *training* – for individuals
* One-to-some = *teaching* – for small groups
* One-to-many = *preaching* – to large crowds

This is the balanced methodology He left for us to follow in Christian ministry.

Application
Many contemporary churches are now rediscovering the enormous benefit of becoming spiritually healthy and balanced. Being healthy requires consistently applying all *three* New Testament methods of ministry in church life.

Jesus first revealed His observational approach to training when He said, *"Follow Me, and I will make you fishers of men."* (Matthew 4:19) He was calling His faithful followers to imitate His example. No one has ever learned how to fish by simply sitting in a classroom. Attaining this new skill requires going where the fish are and actually putting the appropriate bait in the water. Following the Lord's pattern of relational instruction, the apostles soon learned the art of witnessing and disciple-making.

After Pentecost, the Lord's disciples began encouraging and equipping the many highly motivated new believers. Over time, they became effective witnesses who truly lived their faith. Evangelism and disciple-making combined to become the early church's ministry pattern. This resulted in generations of strong, reproducing Christians. The original twelve, minus Judas, were later joined by Barnabas and Paul, who faithfully implemented the Lord's revealed strategy and had multiplying ministries.

Spiritual Growth Assignment:

1. Meet with your teammate before next week's small group and complete the next session in *A Call to Joy*. In preparation for completing Session Six of *A Call to Joy*, both of you will prepare to be leaders using the *A Call to Joy Discipler's Guide*. During your one-to-one meeting, one of you will role play as the *Discipler* and the other as the *Timothy* using the *A Call to Joy Timothy's Guide*. When you complete 1/2 of the session, simply trade roles and finish the rest of the material.

2. Be sure to complete the *Spiritual Growth Assignment* and read the disciple-making chapter at the end of the *A Call to Joy* session. Mark highlights and discuss them with your teammate the following week.

SESSION TEN

DISCIPLE-MAKING IN THE EARLY CHURCH

Early Church Background

After Jesus rose from the dead, He appeared to His disciples and five hundred other believers over a period of 40 days, giving them many convincing proofs that He was alive. Before the Lord ascended back to His Father's heavenly kingdom, He told the disciples to stay in Jerusalem and wait until they received the power of the Holy Spirit. He promised to enable them to become effective witnesses in *"...Jerusalem, and in all Judea and Samaria, and even to the remotest part of the earth."* (Acts 1:8)

They gathered together as Jesus had instructed, and on the day of Pentecost, Jews from many nations were visiting Jerusalem. In fulfillment of Joel 2:28-29, the disciples were filled with the Holy Spirit and began miraculously proclaiming the wonders of God in many languages. Peter then delivered a powerful sermon to the crowd and three thousand people received Christ as their Savior. People began placing their faith in Him on a daily basis, and soon the number reached five thousand believers! From that time on, the number of new converts increased rapidly in the early church.

One of the first century church's leaders was named Stephen, a man full of faith and of the Holy Spirit. As he continually shared the gospel, some of the synagogue members falsely accused him of blasphemy. They brought him before the high priest, but instead of crumbling beneath the pressure, Stephen used this occasion to deliver a passionate sermon about the Messiah.

The unbelieving Jewish leaders were so furious that they dragged Stephen out of the city and threw stones at him until he died. Young Saul of Tarsus, a Pharisee who later became the apostle Paul, watched this entire horrific spectacle and gave his full approval to Stephen's death. This incident ignited great persecution against the church in Jerusalem, and nearly all of the disciples were scattered throughout Judea and Samaria. However, they preached the good news about Jesus wherever they went.

Saul continued seeking to destroy the church, going from house to house and dragging men and women to prison. But something extraordinary happened while he was on his way to Damascus to persecute Christians there:

"...Suddenly a light from heaven flashed around him; and he fell to the ground and heard a voice saying to him, "Saul, Saul, why are you persecuting Me?" And he said, 'Who are you, Lord?' And He said, 'I am Jesus whom you are persecuting.'" (Acts 9:3-5)

Saul humbly became a believer, was baptized, and began to fellowship with the disciples in Damascus, the same disciples he'd previously planned to drag away to prison!

Soon after Saul's conversion, he began proclaiming that Jesus was the Son of God, so the Jews repeatedly conspired to kill him. Protected by the Holy Spirit, he later journeyed to Jerusalem, seeking to meet with the Lord's disciples. This leads us to the ministry of Barnabas, one of the early church's first disciple-makers.

The Ministry of Barnabas

"Joseph, a Levite of Cyprian birth, who was also called Barnabas by the apostles (which translated means Son of Encouragement), and who owned a tract of land, sold it and brought the money and laid it at the apostles' feet." (Acts 4:36-37)

When Paul arrived in Jerusalem, at first the disciples were afraid of him, but Barnabas courageously spoke up on his behalf.

"Barnabas took hold of him [Paul] and brought him to the apostles

and declared to them how on the road he had seen the Lord, and that He [Jesus] had talked to him, and how at Damascus he had spoken out boldly in the name of Jesus." (Acts 9:27)

"Those who were scattered because of the persecution that occurred in connection with Stephen made their way to Phoenicia and Cyprus and Antioch, speaking the word to no one except to Jews alone. But there were some of them, men of Cyprus and Cyrene, who came to Antioch and began speaking to the Greeks also, preaching the Lord Jesus. And the hand of the Lord was with them, and a large number who believed turned to the Lord. The news about them reached the ears of the church at Jerusalem, and they sent Barnabas off to Antioch." (Acts 11:19-22)

"When he arrived and witnessed the grace of God, he rejoiced and began to encourage them all with a resolute heart to remain true to the Lord; for he was a good man, and full of the Holy Spirit and of faith. And considerable numbers were brought to the Lord." (Acts 11:23-24)

When a church provides a life-to-life discipling process designed to equip new converts, witnessing and evangelistic multiplication begin taking place naturally. This is how healthy churches experience steady numerical growth. Multiplication advances through the combined witness of a church's most dedicated existing members and its newest professing believers.

The early church's life-to-life ministry continually produced new generations of spiritual leaders. Through friendship, this relational approach to ministry became the normative experience of first-century Christians.

"He [Barnabas] left for Tarsus to look for Saul; and when he had found him he brought him to Antioch. And for an entire year they met with the church and taught considerable numbers; and the disciples were first called Christians in Antioch." (Acts 11:25-26)

The Ministry of Paul
"Paul and Barnabas stayed in Antioch, teaching and preaching with many others the word of the Lord. After some days Paul said to Barn-

abas, 'Let us return and visit the brethren in every city in which we proclaimed the word of the Lord, and see how they are.'" (Acts 15:35-36)

"Paul came also to Derbe and to Lystra. And a disciple was there named Timothy, the son of a Jewish woman who was a believer, but his father was a Greek, and he was well spoken of by the brethren who were in Lystra and Iconium. Paul wanted this man to go with him." (Acts 16:1-3)

The Ministry of Peter

"Paul and his companions put out to sea from Paphos and came to Perga in Pamphylia; but John [Mark] left them and returned to Jerusalem." (Acts 13:13)

Paul was greatly disappointed when John Mark left to go home in the middle of his first missionary journey. He decided not to give John Mark a second chance. However, Barnabas disagreed and was willing to take John Mark with them again (see Acts 15:36-41).

After John Mark miserably failed on his first missionary journey with Paul and Barnabas, he returned to Jerusalem. Then after a period of spiritual healing, the apostle _____ began investing his time in young John Mark's life.

"She who is in Babylon, chosen together with you, sends you greetings, and so does my son, Mark." (1 Peter 5:13)

It's inspiring to realize that a man who once ran away from his ministry later wrote the first Gospel recorded in the New Testament. What an amazing privilege our Lord gave Mark. His early prominence in Christianity was fully acknowledged in church history. He clearly succeeded spiritually in spite of his initial failure.

"Only Luke is with me. Pick up Mark and bring him with you, for he is useful to me for service." (2 Timothy 4:11)

Relational Ministry

The six teams listed below are biblical examples of disciple-making relationships. In each case, a more mature believer spiritually adopted and trained a younger believer. The mentor's ministry was to help his teammate grow so that he could fulfill his calling.

- Moses and Joshua
- Elijah and Elisha
- Barnabas and Paul
- Paul and Timothy
- Paul and Titus
- Peter and Mark

Spiritual Growth Assignment

Meet with your teammate for this week's life-to-life training session and complete the next session of *A Call to Joy*. In preparation for completing Session Seven of *A Call to Joy*, both of you will prepare to be leaders using the *A Call to Joy Discipler's Guide*. During your one-to-one meeting, one of you will role play as the *Discipler* and the other as the *Timothy* using the *A Call to Joy Timothy's Guide*. When you complete 1/2 of the session, simply trade roles and finish the rest of the material.

SESSION ELEVEN

THE GRADUAL DECLINE OF DISCIPLE-MAKING ACROSS THE CENTURIES

Reviewing Church History

In the centuries following the early church era, many substitutes for personal witnessing and disciple-making began appearing almost unnoticed in the Christian church. The emerging church grew rapidly but over time it became increasingly *institutionalized*.

As Christianity experienced this gradual shift, evangelistic multiplication began to suffer. This unexpected spiritual setback came from within the faith and was related to three primary influences: *depersonalization*, *civil religion*, and *professionalism*. Church history reveals that these growing factors were among Christianity's foremost challenges because they eroded spiritual vitality. The influences that caused this early damage remain with us in varying degrees even today.

Depersonalization – Depersonalization has occurred through the generations when churches or denominations have minimized their practical application of the Bible's instruction concerning the priesthood of the believer.

Depersonalization is often accompanied by the subtle tendency to make the individual needs and ministry potential of Christians less important than the church's structure, rituals, traditions, or programs.

Civil religion – When Emperor Constantine declared himself to be a follower of Jesus Christ, he made Christianity a legal religion in the Roman Empire. Soon after that, it became popular to be called a

87

Christian. However, an authentic understanding of spiritual faith in Christ and personal commitment were often missing, so many who professed to be new Christians sadly remained spiritually lost. During that new era of superficial religion, many ill-informed seekers who needed salvation began relying on religious acts of various kinds rather than on personal faith in the Lord Jesus Himself.

Historically, human effort has often become a substitute for sincere repentance and personal _____ in Jesus Christ. However, the Bible teaches that God's grace and forgiveness are fully and freely available to anyone. Nothing else besides faith in Jesus Christ our Savior can initiate an eternal relationship with His Father (see John 14:21-24; Romans 10:9-10; Ephesians 2:8-9).

Civil religion has always been an enemy of the Christian faith. Whenever we equate anyone's nationality, family history, religious acts, or good works with redeeming faith, we miss the entire point of the cross and resurrection.

By the third century, evangelism was clearly affected by civil religion, and many who were still unredeemed joined Constantine in calling themselves Christians. As long as believers had to worship in hiding and suffer persecution, it wasn't difficult to recognize the genuine disciples of Christ. However, that slowly changed. The arrival of civil religion produced many new unexpected challenges that tended to undermine Christian discipleship.

The spiritual counterfeit of authentic Christianity has always been the _____ of being religious without the inward spiritual reality of actually being redeemed through faith in Jesus Christ. False teachings with no life-giving power are merely sanctimonious sounding words. They're unable to provide anyone with the assurance of salvation. Only by the grace extended through the cross can humankind find forgiveness. Spiritual rebirth alone can provide the certainty of being with our Father in heaven. Merely being religious without personal faith in Jesus Christ leads to false hope. No one wants the emotional turmoil of such self-inflicted spiritual deception. This only leads to continual emptiness and spiritual bondage.

Professionalism – After the church's early centuries of rapid growth, another negative tendency began to develop. This new trend delegated the work of Christian ministry to a few trained Christian professionals. Over time this growing error became synonymous with the expression "Let the clergy do it." Instead of carrying out ministry themselves, church members began thinking, *"We're giving our money, so the church staff can do the work."* This inverted understanding of Christian ministry proved to be in direct opposition with the methodology of the early New Testament church.

As a result of this far-reaching, self-perpetuating error, many church members still remain unprepared to carry out their work even today. Sadly, they're mistakenly expecting others to carry out their God-given ministries for them.

The New Testament Model for Building Spiritual Leaders
In contrast to the unhealthy tendencies we've just reviewed, active participants in the Lord's service are specifically called to multiply by making disciples. For that reason, church leaders are instructed to _____ church members to effectively carry out their individual ministries. Ephesians 2:10 affirms this understanding by saying, *"We are His workmanship, created in Christ Jesus for good works, which God prepared beforehand so that we would walk in them."*

Church leaders' ministries include teaching members how, when, and where to use their spiritual gifts and how to function as valued members in the body of Christ.

The Bible reminds us:
"He gave some as apostles, some as prophets, some as evangelists, and some as pastors and teachers, for the equipping of the saints for the work of service, to the building up of the body of Christ." (Ephesians 4:11-12)

As we rediscover the spiritual power of evangelistic multiplication, we must remember that the primary biblical method for preparing future Christian leaders is through equipping _____.

Caring for New Believers

We can easily see the Lord's great love for new Christians by what He said during His final hours with His first disciples. Thoughtfully consider His discussion with Peter: *"Jesus said to Simon Peter, 'Simon, son of John, do you love Me more than these?' "* Then after Peter's answer Jesus continued, *"Tend My lambs."* This directive specifically referred to caring for the spiritual needs of _____ believers. Next, referring to _____ believers, Jesus said, *"Shepherd My sheep"* and *"Tend My sheep."* (John 21:15-17)

People have always been the primary focus of the Lord's concern, so when we invest our time discipling new believers or other growing Christians, we are personally demonstrating our love for Him. Our actions most meaningfully express our heartfelt devotion and personal gratitude. Disciple-making is the specific ministry which our Lord Jesus requested just before He ascended back to the right hand of His Father, so accomplishing this important task must take priority among the many forms of service in today's church. Some congregations have large numbers, but in spite of what the Lord said, very few church members have ever personally been discipled by a more experienced believer. This is typically why they are not yet multiplying spiritually.

Church-growth experts are alarmed by the massive international attrition rate in today's churches. Millions of unequipped, nominal church members are drifting back into the world each year. This trend is primarily due to neglect and the absence of an intentional New Testament disciple-making *process*.

We're currently being warned about this because a high percentage of new members are quietly leaving unnoticed through their churches' "back doors." When this attrition finally equals a church's evangelistic outreach, they soon begin to plateau.

Strong churches are the result of having spiritually healthy individual members. This is why life-to-life disciple-making will always be needed. In reference to early stages of spiritual growth, Paul explained, *"I gave you milk to drink, not solid food; because you were not yet able to receive it"* (1 Corinthians 3:2). Again in 1 Thessalonians 2:7 he said, *"We proved to be gentle among you, as a nursing mother tenderly cares for her own children."*

Consider the quality of attentiveness a loving parent gives each baby at a time. Now imagine the immense challenge of looking after newborn quintuplets. In that same sense, it requires numerous trained disciple-makers in each church to give new Christians the individual attention which they require. This spiritual need is intensified during the first year of their walk with Christ. This critical period of adjustment calls for a steady stream of fellowship and regular spiritual nutrition. Peter wrote, *"Like newborn babies, long for the pure milk of the word, so that by it you may grow."* (1 Peter 2:2)

With individual nurture, a healthy spiritual diet, and a positive church environment, new believers flourish. Through a sustained, intentional discipling process, they also enjoy the privilege of personally *"growing in respect to salvation."* (1 Peter 2:2) After a few weeks or months, they'll experience the fulfillment of learning to eat balanced spiritual meals on their own. Observably, their spiritual appetite and personal growth will steadily begin to increase. Over time, if properly discipled, they'll progressively move beyond milk to bread, then to meat, and finally they'll understand why *"solid food is for the mature."* (Hebrews 5:14)

Spiritual Growth Assignment:
If you missed one of your one-to-one *A Call to Joy* sessions, use this week to make it up.

SESSION TWELVE

THE PROVEN POWER OF NEW TESTAMENT SPIRITUAL MULTIPLICATION

To illustrate today's study, let's imagine that a man named Charlie moves into our community and joins our church. This is an unusually exciting development because soon after he arrives, he immediately begins leading new friends and acquaintances to Christ. As a result of his prayer life, dedication, and personal witness, let's say that he reaches one new person for Christ every week and continues that pattern for 16 years.

Let's say that Charlie has a dedicated Christian brother named Sam. Imagine that he also moves to our community and soon joins our church. However, he's an even more consistent witness than Charlie and he starts leading someone to Christ every day. Even more amazingly, he faithfully does this for the next 16 years. At the end of that period, he will have reached 5,840 people for the Lord.

Let's say Sam has a highly committed cousin named Floyd. He also relocates to our area, so you're pleased when he joins our church. Honestly, you can hardly wait to see how many people he will lead to Christ. However, to your surprise, you discover that Floyd is totally different from his relatives. He leads only one new friend to Christ in six months, so at first you're a little disappointed. Let's say the new believer's name he reaches is...Timothy.

As Charlie and Sam lead their many friends and acquaintances to Christ, they always appear to be moving fast. They witness effectively but never _____ _____ _____ to disciple those they reach.

Both men are extremely competent, so they always carefully explain the gospel. However, after each new believer prays to receive Christ, they simply recommend our church and move ahead to the next witnessing opportunity. Though they are both highly dedicated, personal disciple-making simply isn't on their minds.

In contrast, you notice that Floyd enjoys spending quality time with Timothy. He personally shows him how to develop spiritually. As a result, Timothy also begins having a daily quiet time, praying, reading the Bible, and sharing his faith with others. Because of Floyd's equipping ministry, Timothy also slowly begins learning how to equip other newer fellow believers. This happens naturally as he enjoys the privilege of observing Floyd's disciple-making _____ .

Floyd continues investing his time in Timothy while everyone else is focused on the amazing evangelistic results which Charlie and Sam are experiencing. Because of Floyd's intentional life-to-life ministry, within about 6 to 12 months, Timothy has the privilege of leading one of his own friends to Christ. Then, following Floyd's example, he begins personally helping that new believer in the same way that Floyd discipled him. As both Floyd and Timothy faithfully continue their lifestyle of daily witness and personally discipling each new Christian who responds, the results become staggering over the decades.

The following chart depicts the powerful impact of spiritual multiplication.

Years	Charlie	Sam	Floyd
	Wins one person each week.	Wins one person each day.	Wins one person each year and disciples him so that he can reproduce the same ministry pattern.
1	52	365	2
2	104	730	4
3	156	1,095	8

5	260	1,825	32
7	364	2,555	128
9	468	3,285	512
11	572	4,015	2,048

Through the New Testament's methodology of life-to-life disciple-making, Floyd has now outpaced Charlie, who has been consistently winning one person to the Lord each week!

| 13 | 676 | 4,745 | 8,192 |

Because Floyd's lifestyle produces spiritual multiplication naturally, he has also passed Sam, who has been leading one person to Christ every day!

15	780	5,475	32,768
17	884	6,205	131,072
19	988	6,935	524,288
33	1,716	12,045	8,589,934,592

If trainees in *each* new spiritual generation faithfully follow Floyd and Timothy's spiritual example, they will have enabled the gospel to be shared with more than eight billion people. That's more than the current population of the world! If thousands and then millions of today's Christians adopt the New Testament's methodology and simply begin praying daily for the opportunity to witness and personally disciple each new believer, the Great Commission can potentially be fulfilled in our century! Our high calling is to devote ourselves to the Lord's service, follow His example, and trust Him for the results.

The early Christian community utilized the methodology of spiritual multiplication during its many decades of dynamic growth. Today that same ministry of multiplication is fully available to every Christian church, as well as to every believer living anywhere in the world.

"One of the first verses of Scripture that Dawson Trotman, founder of the Navigators, encouraged me to memorize was *'The things which you have heard from me in the presence of many witnesses, entrust these to faithful men who will be able to teach others also.'* (2 Timothy 2:2) This is like a mathematical formula for spreading the gospel and enlarging the church. Paul taught Timothy; Timothy shared what he knew with faithful men; these faithful men would then teach others also. And so the process goes on and on. If every believer followed this pattern, the church could reach the entire world with the gospel in one generation! Mass crusades, in which I believe and to which I have committed my life, will never finish the Great Commission; but a one-by-one ministry will." – Dr. Billy Graham

One often unnoticed fact about the early church's equipping methodology is that it required almost no financial ability. This means that today, any dedicated Christian can afford to do it! Through Christ-centered equipping relationships, we can all positively impact our world for Christ no matter where we live. Neither our gender, vocation, or location diminishes our usefulness in terms of disciple-making. Instead, *Christian love, dedication,* and our *time devoted to encouraging and equipping new Christians* is what actually makes the difference.

We can all equip growing disciples for Christ wherever we worship and serve. This is true no matter how old or young we may be. The key to success and satisfaction in our calling rests in meaningfully investing our lives in the lives of others. We are to simply follow the Lord's methodology and advance His kingdom! That's what this course was specifically written to help us accomplish.

Our generation is plagued with a little acknowledged problem: too many of our churches are still unaware that evangelistic multiplication is supposed to be normal. Instead, we're still engaged in multiple short-range programs that merely produce addition. This misses the biblical goal of spiritual multiplication. Unintentionally, they've neglected the Lord's last and highly specific command in Matthew 28:19. Because of the failure to produce multiplying disciples, the global need for change in church life remains urgent. The objective of our class is therefore to help restore New Testament disciple-making to its intended place of importance in Christian ministry.

Through spiritual multiplication, we can each help complete the Lord's last assignment. It's the only methodology that's proven powerful enough to fulfill the Great Commission! The Lord's New Testament methodology can be effectively employed in any church in any country and it is easily initiated through Christian friendship. It simply requires love, time, and spiritual dedication!

"In spite of the fact that our Lord gave His life to rescue mankind from the consequence of sin, it is possible that professing Christians still may not accept what He said about sinners being lost. That of course is dangerous! However, if by faith we do believe what Jesus said about God's judgment and explained about hell, but are still too complacent to care about reaching the millions who are lost, then that selfish sin needs to be forgiven! This sad awareness weighs deeply on my heart. We simply cannot afford to be indifferent about our witness or discipling those who place their faith in Christ." – Billie Hanks Jr.

"What the church needs now is not better methods, but a return to the most basic methodology of the New Testament ... one person discipling another. Men are God's method!" – E. M. Bounds

We encourage you to enlist one or more of your most dedicated Christian friends to attend *Becoming A Disciple-Maker*. Now that the ministry vision has been cast, it's time for us to go to work. Let's *"make disciples..."* (Matthew 28:19) in preparation for the Lord's return!

THE VISION FOR SPIRITUAL MULTIPLICATION

"And this gospel of the kingdom will be preached in the whole world as a testimony to all nations, and then the end will come."
(Matthew 24:14)

On a sunny Florida afternoon years ago, I heard the haunting and unforgettable words of a leading evangelical British minister who said, "Mark my words, North American Christians: Your large church buildings will be as empty as the cathedrals of Great Britain within a span of twenty-five to fifty years if you do not change your methodology."

The well known cleric spoke with the assurance of a prophet, yet the humility of one who had been mellowed by many years of Christian service.

Our Traditional Methodology

After hearing the English pastor speak, I decided to investigate his claims. In subsequent years, I spent considerable time in England and in Europe and learned to appreciate the wisdom of his words. I discovered striking similarities between declining spiritual vitality and decreasing church membership in Great Britain decades ago and what we are seeing in large segments of the church in North American today.

We must resist the temptation to rely on the baptism of our church children to exonerate us from our larger call to national and world evangelization, and we must carefully re-examine our own methods of evangelism to see whether they are based on tradition or on the Bible. Our almost exclusive dependence on evangelism by addition through preaching is reminiscent of the days when throngs of people listened to the eloquent messages of such greats as England's Charles Haddon Spurgeon.

The academic instruction of our Christian leaders at the seminary level continues to focus on theological concepts and scholarship while all but overlooking practical instruction in how to equip laypeople for their ministries. As a result, few laypeople know how to evangelize, nurture, or disciple anyone. At a time when the world birthrate is growing faster than at any other point in history, the absence of the concept of apprenticeship in equipping the laity at the local church level all but ensures a serious, long-range decline in church membership.

One day while I was working in the Billy Graham crusade in London, I was invited to lunch by one of England's leading young evangelists. Over the meal we discussed evangelism in our two countries and denominations, comparing various approaches and methods from his Anglican perspective and my Southern Baptist background. After graciously complimenting my denomination as one of the world's most evangelistic, he asked me a most penetrating question: "What percentage of your Baptist laity would normally win someone to Jesus Christ during any given year?"

At that point, I wished he had asked about our generous giving to missions, our popular evangelistic conferences, or our successful city-wide crusades, but he had asked a question that was most embarrassing.

I had to tell him that even in our best years, fewer than 5 percent of the laity and clergy combined lead anyone to a saving knowledge of Christ. We simply do not have enough trained workers. We have an army of unequipped people who are sympathetic with evangelism, but only a few who are participating in the joy of the harvest. Many bystanders are praying for these workers and they appreciate what the workers are doing, and even help pay their wages, but they do not know how to participate in the harvest.

As I have traveled and ministered as the guest of numerous Christian groups, I have discovered that this is the unsolved problem of evangelism worldwide. Too few are doing the work of many in evangelism. Consciously or unconsciously, we have wasted our most valuable resource: the laity.

Relying on our traditional approach, which neglects personal follow-up and fails to utilize our more mature laypeople, we are plagued with a growing attrition rate, no matter how successful our short-range evangelistic efforts appear to be. Because of this unattended problem, large percentages of our congregations are totally inactive, and many members cannot even be found. Obviously, the new converts who never grow will never win another to Christ. It needs to be understood that evangelism's most persistent enemy is poorly planned and poorly executed follow-up.

The Evangelized as Evangelizers

The real issue involved in making disciples is international in scope and is critical in terms of the future of the church. The task of education and motivating Christian leaders to equip the laity for a lifestyle of ministry is far larger than what any single denomination, organization, or program can accomplish. Something of this magnitude requires the joint effort of all Christians and a return to the Biblical principles used by the early church.

Since theological education is the pacesetter in evangelism and methodology, it bears a major responsibility and obligation to be balanced, practical, and Scripturally sound in its approach to disciple-making. The need is urgent because the methods we have inherited from tradition are simply not working in terms of the Great Commission. We must learn from the failures of the past and open our minds to the fact that once-Christian parts of the world now desperately need to be re-evangelized. The best methods of our Reformation forefathers were not enough to sustain evangelism from generation to generation.

We must take strategic steps in our churches, colleges, and seminaries to ensure that Christians of this generation receive instruction in how to have a quality ministry of spiritual multiplication. Herschel H. Hobbs wisely said, "The work of evangelism is never complete until the evangelized becomes the evangelizer." Amplifying this statement, if the process of making disciples is to be complete, all new Christians should be trained to be active in evangelism themselves. This full-circle apprenticeship process requires time, love, discipline, and personal instruction. The added work of discipleship is well worth the investment, because the fruit remains and multiplies!

The church's great evangelistic task will be carried out only when we update our philosophy of ministry through a re-examination of the principles revealed in the ministry of Christ. The gospels show us that Jesus trained His disciples by *association* before giving them the Great Commission. Being *with Him* was their primary means of learning how to minister. Mark tells us, *"He appointed twelve - designating them apostles - that they might be with Him and that He might send them out to preach."* (Mark 3:14)

The disciples' evangelism grew out of a lifestyle seasoned by many hours in Jesus' presence. They were apprenticed in real-life situations. They saw evangelism, counseling, preaching, teaching, and every other form of ministry firsthand.

Jesus' pattern was, *"Come, follow Me...and I will make you fishers of men."* (Matthew 4:19) He *showed them* how to minister. By contrast, as church leaders we typically *tell people* why they ought to minister, but fail to show them how.

Great preaching and teaching are absolutely vital, but they cannot replace the apprenticing concept demonstrated by Christ. The critical need of the modern church does not involve moving away from preaching and teaching, but it does require re-establishing a New Testament concept of apprenticeship.

Under pastoral leadership committed to this revitalized approach, church members will be trained and shown how to carry out their God-given ministries. Until his happens, widespread evangelistic multiplication will not occur in the church and the average believer will never know the joy of leading another person to Christ.

Taking God's Mandate Seriously

The burden of my heart is to see the concept of multiplying disciples restored to our churches, because it alone has the realistic potential of actually reaching every nation in the world with the gospel.

Our present short-range course of action more often that not breeds a sense of frustration and spiritual fatigue in the lives of faithful Christian workers. Because of the lack of a long-range strategy, many pastors and staff members find themselves totally absorbed in a multitude of good activities to the exclusion of the best. We find no time for training our lay leaders for the work of the ministry. This omission leaves the pastor and his staff members without a strong base of qualified laypeople to labor together with them in the ministries of the local church. As a result, the paid staff carry out the church's follow-up, counseling, hospital visitation, and evangelistic ministries largely on their own.

Since many Christian workers feel that their time is too valuable for personal involvement in equipping our lay leadership, the vicious cycle repeats itself again and again. We are always too busy to follow Jesus' example. We need to come to grips with the fact that – *the Lord revealed His personal pattern of ministry by investing His maximum time in the lives of those who would bear the maximum responsibility in the future ministry of the church.*

One morning I received a call from a friend who pastored the largest church in his county. After three years of ministry there, he was discouraged and wanted to move on to another church field. He asked me to pray with him about the matter and to recommend him to another church if I felt led to do so.

I asked whether he had tried investing a portion of his time in the lives of some of his key laymen. He replied, "I don't have one layman who would be interested."

I told him I felt sure that in a congregation of five hundred, there must be several persons who would respond to the challenge of one-to-one training in spiritual growth and evangelism. I then asked him why he wanted to leave.

"My people are not spiritual," he replied. "Sunday attendance fluctuates with the weather, and our Sunday school teachers are so irresponsible they do not even notify their classes when they miss."

"If that is a justification for leaving a church," I told him, "half the pastors in America would have a reason to resign." I challenged him again to start looking for a faithful man to train.

Six weeks later he called again. I will always remember his enthusiasm. He literally shouted over the phone, "Billie, praise God, I've found three men! I meet with one on Mondays, with another on Tuesday, and with the third on Thursdays. Two are members of my church, and the third is from another church in town."

I knew the pastor of the other church and suggested that my friend obtain his permission to disciple his layman.

He laughed and said, "I've already talked with him, and he said that if I could do anything with him - I could have him!"

"Do you still want me to recommend you to another church?" I asked.

"Definitely not!" he replied. "You couldn't move me out of here with a crowbar!"

As we talked, I discovered that Sunday school had not changed, church attendance still fluctuated, and the overall circumstances were pretty much the same as before. What had changed? Three men were meeting God for a daily quiet time, memorizing Scripture, forming new priorities in their lives, and beginning to share their faith naturally as a lifestyle.

My friend was exuberant because he was now fulfilled through what was happening in these men's lives. They were the beginning of a bright new era in his ministry. Through this experience, he learned to make a higher-quality investment of his time.

Our lack of training through apprenticeship leaves vast numbers of laypeople unfulfilled, because their spiritual gifts are never developed and remain unused. These people fail to receive a workable strategy for personal spiritual growth and evangelism, so they settle into a life of churchmanship rather then disciple-making. In many instances, they are left wide open to an assortment of false doctrines that thrive on the Biblical ignorance of immature but well-meaning church members who never received the sound instruction or loving care of a more mature Christian.

If we will learn to be with people, equipping them as Jesus did, and long to see new Christians perfected in Christ as Paul and Barnabas did (Acts 14:21-23) our generation can expect to see the greatest multiplication of converts and congregations since the early days of the Christian church.

Love, vision, personal discipline, and the willingness to accept mutual accountability are the critical factors needed for a lifestyle that produces spiritual multipliers. Until pastors, missionaries, and other Christian leaders take seriously God's mandate to equip His people for ministry, Christ's second coming will be postponed. His return is dependent on world evangelization (Matthew 24:14) and world evangelization is dependent on His saints being equipped for their ministries.

Every pastor and layperson can have a vital part in changing the statistics that show we are currently losing the world. It is we who are shaping the foundation of the future church, just as the Reformers once molded and shaped the church we love today. The awesome reality is that, God has committed the spiritual destiny of the entire world to our hands. We dare not fail!

The gauntlet of leadership has been passed to our generation and we must make an important decision regarding methodology. Every year that passes makes the right decision even more critical. A rising percentage of the world's population does not yet know Jesus Christ!

We stand at a crossroad. However good our method of addition has been, it has not been good enough. By itself, it has proved inadequate.

Today's situation calls for a new vision and a return to a fully absorbed New Testament philosophy of ministry. We must harness the power of evangelistic multiplication and commit ourselves to the long-range strategy of equipping all the Lord's people to be spiritual reproducers.

We have the Word of God, the Holy Spirit, two thousand years of church history, and the privilege of prayer as our resources for making the right decision. At this moment…the choice is yours.

DISCIPLE-MAKING
AND THE CHRISTIAN
CHURCH

"'Come follow Me,' Jesus said,
and I will make you fishers of men.'"
(Matthew 4:19)

Distinguishing Teaching from Training

Many of the church's past failures in evangelism have resulted from attempting to impart through *teaching*, skills that can best be instilled in one's spiritual life through *training*. Historically, knowledge has always been transferred through one of these two complementary but distinctively different forms of education – *teaching* and *training*.

Teaching focuses on the transmission of knowledge and concepts. Therefore, an outstanding teacher can effectively convey information to tens, hundreds, or even thousands of people. Typically, facts, examples, and stories are used to express their thoughts. If they are gifted, they will need nothing else but words to get their point across. Our Lord was a master teacher; His illustrations and parables remain without equal. The size of the groups He taught had no bearing on the timeless impact which His teaching produced. His uniqueness came from His ability to unforgettably present spiritual truth with authority and profound clarity. He was equally comfortable teaching a small group of twelve or addressing a gathering of over five thousand. His amazing delivery during the Sermon on the Mount demonstrates the reality that groups of all sizes can successfully be taught.

Training is different from teaching because it requires *observation*. Simply stated, *training focuses on the transmission of learned skills*. The term that best communicates this highly practical on-the-job training process is apprenticeship. Because observation and personal experience are needed for effective training, one-to-one relationships are universally utilized as the most accepted format for skill related instruction.

Let's use aviation to illustrate the difference between these two well known methods of instruction. One summer I was flying in a small private airplane with a close friend who was a highly experienced flight instructor. Having spent little time flying in a small aircraft myself, I became a bit concerned as we crossed a rugged mountain range in New Mexico. What would happen if my friend had a heart attack while we were flying? I suggested that he take a few minutes to instruct me on the basics of "safely" crash landing an airplane.

As we talked, Wortley Rudd asked, "Billie, do you know why I am so convinced about the effectiveness of personal disciple-making?"

"No, but I would like to," I replied.

"When you go to flight school," he said, "you are literally discipled in how to fly an aircraft. Your basic instruction is usually conducted on the ground in a small group. While in that setting you are *taught* the basic concepts of aerodynamics; but later, after ground school, most of your actual *training* takes place in the air while sitting next to an experienced pilot. You repeatedly observe his or her example while following their instructions. Every pilot in the air has been individually *trained* in how to fly." One-to-one instruction is highly effective in today's aeronautics and it functioned the same way in the early church's equipping ministry.

In Jesus' personal experience of disciple-making, He was sometimes with His disciples in a group, and on other occasions He was with them individually. He discipled His Apostles using both methods of communication and ultimately they became highly successful fishers of men.

The same principle of observation holds true in the practice of medicine. Typically, surgeons who perform the most delicate types of surgery are required to have the longest and most specialized internships. In general, the more critical the consequence of failure, the greater the need for thorough individual training. If for no reason other than this – training in personal evangelism, which involves eternity, deserves our best and most committed dedication. From the earliest days of the Lord's ministry, He personally showed us by the high priority which He placed on relational training. *"As Jesus was walking beside the Sea of Galilee, he saw two brothers, Simon called Peter and his brother Andrew. They were casting a net into the lake, for they were fishermen. 'Come, follow Me,' Jesus said, 'and I will make you fishers of men.' At once they left their nets and followed Him."* (Matthew 4:18-20) Their on-the-job training had begun!

One summer, while on vacation in Colorado, I experienced a vivid illustration of training by observation. On this particular day, I had been attempting to do some trout fishing. Although I had tried hard, the fish had simply not cooperated! Having had no success, I realized I needed some expert help.

Soon after that, I started looking for an instructor – who could show me how to fish. I was introduced to an experienced fly fisherman and he agreed to train me in the art. He spent a brief time introducing me to the "ins and outs" of the sport. I first learned the difference between a "dry" fly and a "wet" fly. This was my initial *teaching* period which focused on the theory of fly fishing.

Then he said, "Let's take one of these flies, attach it to a line, and go out in the front yard where we can actually practice casting." I was now moving from *teaching* to *training* by applying the knowledge I had gained.

I spent several minutes casting the little fly toward a nearby yellow flower until I could land it near the daisy nearly every time. He then went into his garage and brought out a pair of hip high wading boots. I put them on, and he had me walk around the yard repeatedly casting the fly.

Having given me this basic "on-shore" instruction, my trainer said, "Now you are ready for the real thing."

I thought he would take me to a quiet little stream like the one where I had been fishing. To my surprise, however, we arrived at a wide, rushing mountain stream where he knew the fish were plentiful. I immediately learned something important through this experience! In our evangelism, many of us don't reach people simply because we are fishing in the wrong places. We are more concerned about the beauty and convenience of our fishing spots than the ultimate success of our mission.

My instructor said, "Just follow me."

He stepped out into the water which quickly became rather deep, so he turned around and gave me a few practical pointers. "Billie," he said, "Don't ever step on a rock until you test it. Put your foot on it first, then try to move it to see if it will roll under the force of the water and your weight. Next, slide your foot over the surface of the rock to check for moss which might cause you to slip. When you cast, watch out for those low hanging tree limbs on the right. Notice the way I cast under them."

I followed his example to the letter and quickly caught several nice rainbow trout. This was a tremendous improvement over my previous experience. What made the difference? First, I was under the guidance of an experienced fisherman. Second, I was *taught* the basic concepts of fly fishing before entering the water. Third, he personally *trained* me by *example* showing me where and how to fish. I was actually apprenticed by following him into the rushing stream. Through this training, I was now using the right fly in the right stream at the best possible time of day for successful results!

Authentic disciple-making requires being balanced and combining methods of instruction. Some knowledge is best conveyed through *teaching* while other knowledge is best conveyed through *training* because one method deals with *concepts*, the other method deals with learned *skills*.

The Principle Applied in Church Ministries

Unfortunately, many churches are still attempting to assimilate their new members without giving them the benefit of individual one-to-one, life-to-life training. Because of this oversight, church leaders are now asking how they can most effectively correct this ongoing need.

Some years ago, I received a phone call from California's Southern Baptist Evangelism Director. He was struggling with this same state-wide problem. After earnest prayer, we decided to conduct a pilot project designed to implement an intentional process of life-to-life new member assimilation. We prayed for a process that would produce evangelistic multiplication naturally.

Seventy regionally selected churches took part in this extensive research endeavor. By the end of the fifth year, certified trainers from 238 churches had joined us for what was then North America's largest and longest pilot in life-to-life new member assimilation. This five year experiment in New Testament disciple-making helped us understand and validate the spiritual concepts being presented in this course.

Step One – *A Call to Joy*. We learned that several weeks of immediate life-to-life training including inspirational daily quiet-time reading, along with weekly small-group Bible study, and corporate worship, produced outstanding spiritual results. The *friendship factor* pulled all these equipping experiences together and produced a strong sense of belonging among the rapidly growing new members. We learned that *people were searching for true friends, not just friendly churches*. This is why the relational factor must be at the very heart of any meaningful approach to new-member assimilation. During this life-to-life equipping process, discussions about individual felt needs occurred naturally in the context of each caring disciple-making relationship.

Step Two – *A Call to Growth*. As hoped, we discovered that this deeper level of training proved to be even more effective than the initial instruction. It focused on the basic Christian doctrines, prayer, lifestyle witnessing, and building enjoyable devotional skills.

When *A Call to Joy* and *A Call to Growth* were experienced in sequence, the new church members moved naturally from assurance to spiritual growth, to effective service. Charles Finney, the renowned nineteenth-century evangelist was motivated to write this same process as he observed the spiritual needs of new believers of his day.

> "When the hearts of converts are warm with their first love, then is the time to help them become fully acquainted with their Savior, to hold Him up in all of His grandeur, so as to break away from all self-dependence and to receive Christ as their present, perfect, and everlasting Savior."

> "Unless this course is taken, their backsliding is inevitable. You might as well expect to roll back the waters of Niagara Falls as to stay the tide of their former habits. Surrounded as they are with temptation, they need a deep, thorough and experiential acquaintance with the Savior. *If they are left to their own resources* to stand against temptation instead of being directed to the Savior, they are certain to become discouraged and fall into bondage."

As we seek to deal with these same issues in our era, we need, like Sam Jones, the beloved country preacher, to *pray* earnestly for a heart of genuine concern. Pastor Jones said, "I never see a poor, weak brother that I don't want to keep him away from temptation and help him stay on the straight and narrow way until he gets his feet firmly planted on the ground. New believers need nursing, they need our help. Oh, what's the use of bringing them into the church if nobody takes care of them? My dear brethren, you who are spiritual, love the new convert. Stand by him or her, and do your best for them."

People of all ages can learn to meet the needs of new Christians and prayerfully minister to them as a disciple-maker. A friend once told me a memorable story about a grandmother in a wheelchair. She was individually meeting daily with different younger Christian ladies. She did this five days each week. Her lack of mobility did not keep her from using her kitchen table as an uplifting place of ministry. She used *A Call to Joy* and *A Call to Growth* with one new church member per day and faithfully equipped them to grow and multiply spiritually.

Age makes no difference and being home bound is not a hindrance. Some of the best life-to-life ministry taking place today is being carried out by dedicated Christian retirees who are challenged in various ways, but have rich experience, Biblical knowledge, and the valuable wisdom that comes from years spent with Christ. Seniors are uniquely prepared to encourage and equip a church's growing new believers.

Teenagers can also effectively minister to other teenagers and often have just the right words to help new members in their age group. Those of all ages having lost close friends or loved ones can assist those who are currently experiencing the pain of loneliness. A *Christ-centered friendship* knows no limits in terms of race, education, culture, or background, so your next step is to pray, prepare, and trust God to lead you to the specific trainee of His choice. If we commit ourselves to helping just one or two people each year, new Christians will not flounder. They are looking for a tangible expression of Christ's love. By offering New Testament disciple-making, both we and the new members of our church can grow and multiply!

"Still other seed fell on good soil. It came up, grew and produced a crop, some multiplying thirty, some sixty, some a hundred times."
(Mark 4:8)

RESOURCE SECTION

To obtain resources and current pricing, please visit our web site at www.ieaom.org, call (800) 880-1350 or (254) 947-3030.

Church Starter Pack includes the *Church Implementor's Booklet, Becoming A Disciple-Maker Leader's Pack, Operation Multiplication Workshop 4-CD set*, and toll free consultation.

Becoming a Disciple-Maker Leader's Pack includes a *Becoming A Disciple-Maker Leader's Guide and Student's Guide*, the *A Call to Joy Discipler's* and *Timothy's Guides, A Call to Growth Discipler's* and *Timothy's Guides, Spiritual Journal*, 4 *Steps to Peace with God* evangelistic booklets.

Becoming A Disciple-Maker Student's Pack includes a *Becoming A Disciple-Maker Student's Guide*, the *A Call to Joy Discipler's* and *Timothy's Guides, A Call to Growth Discipler's* and *Timothy's Guides, Spiritual Journal*, 4 *Steps to Peace with God* evangelistic booklets.

Becoming A Disciple-Maker Invitation Brochure.

Becoming A Disciple-Maker Invitation Flyer.

A Call to Joy Timothy's Pack – includes *Timothy's Guide, Spiritual Journal*, and 2 *Steps to Peace with God* evangelistic booklets.

A Call to Growth Timothy's Pack – includes *Timothy's Guide, Spiritual Journal*, and 2 *Steps to Peace with God* evangelistic booklets.

Graduate Discipler's Pack – includes the *A Call to Joy Discipler's Guide, A Call to Growth Discipler's Guide, Spiritual Journal*, and 2 *Steps to Peace with God* evangelistic booklets.

Spiritual Journal

Steps To Peace with God **Booklet** – (Pack of 25)
Discipler's **Graduation Diplomas** – (Packs of 10)
A Call to Joy **Graduation Diplomas** – (Packs of 10)
A Call to Growth **Graduation Diplomas** – (Packs of 10)
Four Part Decision Forms – (Packs of 100)

Operation Multiplication Workshop 4 CD set - Billie Hanks Jr. presents the Biblical basis for "Operation Multiplication." Sessions include: "The Vision for Making Disciples," "The Power of Evangelistic Multiplication," "Equipping Disciple-makers," and "Assimilating New Believers and Members."
Operation Multiplication Workshop 4 Cassette set

Disciple-Making Brochure
Assured of Heaven - Audio-Witnessing CD
The Great Commission "Evangelistic Multiplication" CD – Billie Hanks, Jr.

SCRIPTURE MEMORY PACKETS
Scripture Memory Packet – 52 Scripture verses packed in a leatherette holder. Scripture versions available: **NASB NIV NKJV KJV**

FEATURED BOOKS
Born To Reproduce **Booklet** (NavPress)
Discipleship (Dr. William Shell/Billie Hanks Jr.)
If You Love Me (Billie Hanks, Jr.)
Everyday Evangelism (Billie Hanks Jr.)
The Gift of Giving (Wayne Watts)
The Master Plan of Evangelism (Robert E. Coleman)
     with Study Guide by Roy J. Fish
Quiet Times In Luke (Dan Nelson/Billie Hanks Jr.)
My Spiritual Diary for children ages 7 – 10

Wide Margin Bible
New American Standard Wide-Margin Bibles (NASB)

The NASB is considered the most literal word-for-word accurate translation of the Bible in the English language. These single column wide-margin Bibles include a 1 3/4" wide margin on each page for recording Bible study insights and applications, a large 9 point type size, concordance, and 16 full page maps. Each page is 6 1/8" x 9 1/4".

Hardcover   or   Burgundy Bonded Leather

Concordances
NASB Exhaustive Concordance

A must for every serious Bible student. Locate even the most obscure Scripture verses quickly and easily. Every word in the NASB is listed alphabetically and referenced in order of appearance to every book, chapter, and verse of the Bible. It contains 400,000 entries, and a Hebrew/Aramaic and Greek dictionary that traces words in the NASB text to their equivalents in the original Bible languages for a better understanding of their meaning and application.

NIV Exhaustive Concordance

A must for every serious Bible student. Locate even the most obscure Scripture verses quickly and easily. Complete alphabetical exhaustive listings for every word in the NIV in Biblical order, thorough dictionary-indexes define every Hebrew, Aramaic, and Greek word in the Bible.

The *Be Series*

With over 3 million sold, Warren Wiersbe's *Be Series* has become America's best selling Bible study guide.

The Complete New Testament (23 books)

Matthew – *Be Loyal*

Mark – *Be Diligent*

Luke 1-13 – *Be Compassionate*

Luke 14-24 – *Be Courageous*

John 1-12 – *Be Alive*

John 13 - 21 – *Be Transformed*

Acts 1-12 – *Be Dynamic*

Acts 13-28 – *Be Daring*

Romans – *Be Right*

1 Corinthians – *Be Wise*

2 Corinthians – *Be Encouraged*

Galatians – *Be Free*

Ephesians – *Be Rich*

Philippians – *Be Joyful*

Colossians – *Be Complete*

1&2 Thessalonians – *Be Ready*

1&2 Timothy, Titus, Philemon –
Be Faithful

Hebrews – *Be Confident*

James – *Be Mature*

1 Peter – *Be Hopeful*

2 Peter, 2&3 John, Jude – *Be Alert*

1 John – *Be Real*

Revelation – *Be Victorious*

The Complete Old Testament (27 books)

Genesis 1-11 – *Be Basic*

Genesis 12-24 – *Be Obedient*

Genesis 25-50 – *Be Authentic*

Exodus – *Be Delivered*

Leviticus – *Be Holy*

Numbers – *Be Counted*

Deuteronomy – *Be Equipped*

Joshua – *Be Strong*

Judges – *Be Available*

Ruth & Esther – *Be Committed*

1 Samuel – *Be Successful*

2 Samuel & 1 Chronicles –
Be Restored

1 Kings – *Be Responsible*

2 Kings & 2 Chronicles –
Be Distinct

Ezra, Haggai, Zachariah,
Lamentations – *Be Heroic*

Nehemiah – *Be Determined*

Job – *Be Patient*

Psalm 1-89 – *Be Worshipful*

Psalm 90-150 – *Be Exultant*

Proverbs – *Be Skillful*

Ecclesiastes – *Be Satisfied*

Isaiah – *Be Comforted*

Jeremiah – *Be Decisive*

Ezekiel – *Be Reverent*

Daniel – *Be Resolute*

Hosea. Joel, Jonah, Nahum,
Habakkuk, Malachi – *Be Amazed*

Amos, Obadiah, Micah, Zephaniah
– *Be Concerned*